Metalcraft

E. J. WYNTER M.C.C. Ed.
HEAD OF THE BOYS' CRAFT DEPARTMENT
HAZELWICK COMPREHENSIVE SCHOOL, CRAWLEY, SUSSEX

All the illustrations are by the author

LONGMAN

LONGMAN GROUP LIMITED
London
Associated companies, branches and representatives
throughout the world

© Longman Group Limited 1966, 1971

First published 1966
This edition 1971
Second impression 1973

ISBN 0 582 21137 9

Printed in Hong Kong by
Peninsula Press Ltd

Preface

The aim of this book is to provide a sound theoretical knowledge of the normal workshop practice found in most school metalwork rooms. It includes the range of tools, materials and processes covering forgework, the lathe, sheet metalwork, beaten metalwork, bench work and casting and embraces the standard required by the regional C.S.E. Examining Boards. By keeping the technology to this broad level and avoiding anything of an advanced nature it is hoped to stimulate the curiosity of boys without bewildering them.

Until a person understands the materials and processes of his craft and has a reasonable proficiency with the tools he is unlikely to design anything worth while and still less likely to be able to make it. It is hoped therefore that the following chapters will provide the necessary groundwork to enable boys to understand metalcraft and start them off on lines of thought and enquiry which will lead to the designing and making of things giving lasting pleasure.

In this new edition the text and drawings have been metricated where necessary to conform with SI (Système International d'Unités) basic units. Chapter 6 has been revised to include metric threads and chapter 13 contains new drawings of the metric vernier and micrometer together with examples.

The appendix includes a comprehensive table showing the tapping drill sizes, both recommended and alternative for a wide range of metric thread diameters in both coarse and fine series. It should be remembered that the coarse series is intended for general use, the fine series being used only for work requiring a very fine pitch. Sheet metal gauges in the metric sizes are still under consideration by tool manufacturers so a conversion table has been included showing the thickness in millimetres (to two decimal places) of a popular range of I.S.W.G. sizes. Finally, a comparison chart showing the relationship between metric and other threads has been included in the belief that it will help the craftsman to compare at a glance.

No doubt there will be some frustration and confusion before the colossal task of metricating is complete, but the problems will be simplified by thinking metric.

E. J. WYNTER 1970

v

Contents

Contents

Acknowledgements

For permission to reproduce diagrams we are indebted to the following:

Abingdon King Dick for figure 184 (King Dick); The Aluminium Development Association, *Aluminium Foundry Work for Schools* for figure 175; Rabone Chesterman Ltd. for figure 144; J. Dearden, *Iron and Steel Today*, Oxford University Press (1943) for figures 2, 3 and 8; T. R. Ellin Ltd. for figure 184 (footprint wrench); B. Elliot & Co. Ltd. for figure 185; Moore and Wright (Sheffield) Ltd. for figure 141; James Neill & Co. (Sheffield) Ltd. for figures 21 and 44; Tom Senior (Liversedge) Ltd. for figure 190; Stanley Tools for figure 68.

We are indebted to the following for permission to reproduce copyright material:

British Standards Institution for an adapted extract from *BS 3643 'ISO metric screw threads': Part 1: 1963* 'Thread data and standard thread series' and a table 'Tapping drill sizes' (metric units) compiled from *Supplement No 1 (1967) to BS 1157: 1965*; GKN Screws & Fasteners Limited for part of 'Diameter Comparison Chart'; Easterbrook Allcard & Company Limited for an adapted extract from the *Presto Screwing Tools Catalogue*.

I

Iron and Steel

Iron is found in the earth's crust in the form of a compound of oxygen and iron, known as an ore. Magnetite, red hematite and brown hematite are the richest ores, containing from 40 to 70 per cent iron, and mixed with clay and soil known in the industry as the gangue. Lying just beneath the earth's surface, these ores are obtained by quarrying.

All compounds can be broken down into the separate elements of which they are composed, the process being called decomposition. Chemical action of some sort is required, and to extract iron from its ore the chemical action is fire, and this particular process is called SMELTING. The removal of oxygen from a compound is known as reducing, and anything which releases oxygen from a compound is called a reducing agent. The BLAST FURNACE is used for reducing most ores, the reducing agent being the fuel gas.

The Blast furnace, Fig. 1.

The blast furnace is a tower-like structure from 24 m to 30 m or more in height. It is made of 13 mm thick steel plates and lined inside with firebricks. The raw materials, iron ore, limestone and coke, are carefully weighed and charged in turn into the top of the furnace from a small wagon called a SKIP. A double bell-like arrangement fixed in a casing at the top enables charging to be done with minimum heat loss. The upper bell opens downwards and the charge drops through to fall on the bottom bell. The upper bell closes and the bottom bell opens, admitting the charge to the furnace. In addition, so as to keep the 'burden' in the furnace evenly distributed, the casing, or hopper as it is called, moves round slightly for each fresh charge.

The hot air blast roars in through a number of nozzles placed at intervals round the circumference. This is the hottest part of the furnace and must be water cooled.

FUEL

The fuel is coke because it is strong and can withstand the heavy burden inside the blast furnace so does not choke up as would coal.

AIR BLAST

As the hot gas leaves the furnace it flows through towers containing firebricks built up in a chequer pattern. These towers, known as COWPER'S STOVES, are used to heat the compressed air before it enters the furnace.

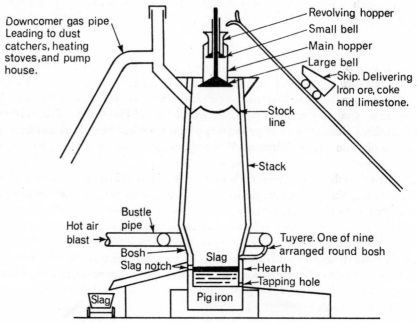

Downcomer gas pipe
Leading to dust
catchers, heating
stoves,and pump
house.

Revolving hopper

Small bell

Main hopper

Large bell

Skip. Delivering
Iron ore, coke
and limestone.

Stock
line

Stack

Hot air
blast

Bustle
pipe

Bosh

Slag notch

Slag

Tuyere. One of nine
arranged round bosh

Hearth

Tapping hole

Slag

Pig iron

Fig. 1   The blast furnace

LIMESTONE

Limestone is used to make a liquid slag of the earthy matter of the ore and coke ash, which then floats on top of the molten iron collecting in the well of the furnace.

THE ACTION IN THE BLAST FURNACE

In the bosh, carbon monoxide results from the burning of coke in the air blast and this gas reduces the iron oxide to iron, the oxygen joining the carbon monoxide to form carbon dioxide. This is the final stage of a process which begins right up in the stack. As the carbon dioxide speeds through the furnace it reacts with the hot coke to form carbon monoxide, which promptly reduces some oxygen from the ore in its path. This constant change from CO to CO_2 and back again as the gas comes in contact first with the ore and then the coke continues throughout the passage of the blast gas in the furnace.

Tapping

The iron and the slag are drawn off separately at intervals throughout the day and night, the process being known as tapping.

SLAG

The slag floats on top of the molten iron and is drawn off to run down a channel cut in sand from which it pours into a wagon. Once regarded as waste, slag now has several uses such as for road making.

IRON

The iron is run off into channels in the sand called 'sows', from which it flows into smaller channels called 'PIGS'. These names came from the resemblance to a sow with a litter of pigs, hence the term 'pig iron'. With increased production and the need for land economy, it is usual now to use a pig casting machine. This consists of an endless chain of small buckets, lime washed to prevent the iron from sticking, each of which is filled with molten pig iron from the furnace. Water spraying quickly cools the metal for tipping out.

A still better method employed by a plant where blast furnaces and steel works run together is to transfer the molten pig iron to a large gas heated 'mixer' furnace where it is kept molten until required.

CAST IRON

Cast iron is a hard, strong but brittle metal. It is easily melted, flows well into intricate moulds and is reasonably cheap. In compression it is superior to any other ordinary metal but is weak in tension. This is due to the large amount of 'free' carbon scattered throughout the metal in the form of graphite.

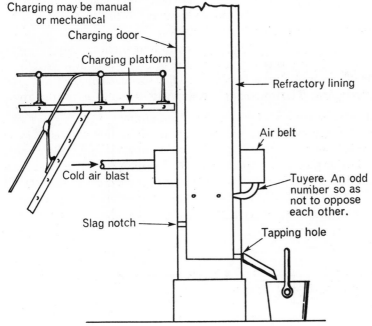

Fig. 2   The cupola

Cast iron is popular and is in great demand for the quick, simple and easy manufacture of parts which would be difficult if not impossible to forge, or would require the careful fitting and assembly of several pieces of metal. It is often much easier to make a wooden pattern and cast the required article in the mould. Such items include switch-box covers, sink covers, lamp posts, brackets of every description, vices, all kinds of machine parts, manhole covers and engine cylinder blocks, to name just a few.

Cast iron is made by remelting pig iron together with carefully graded scrap metal in a cupola, Fig. 2. The fuel is coke and a little limestone is added to flux away the impurities. Melting is necessary to refine the pig iron by adjusting the composition of its elements.

WROUGHT IRON

Wrought iron is fibrous in structure and was once used for all the purposes for which we now use mild steel, such as bolts, shafts, wire and tubes. During its manufacture it develops long dark lines caused by slag streaks, and this is a source of weakness in the metal. Sheet wrought iron, for example, will bend allright across the fibres, but invariably breaks when bent along their length.

The metal contains only a trace of carbon but is regarded for all practical purposes as being carbon free. This enables it to be raised to a very bright heat at the forge, where it can also be easily welded and wrought to the most complicated shape without injury or damage. Wrought iron can withstand tension and shock loads extremely well and for this reason has always been favoured for use as anchor cables, chains and railway couplings. Very little wrought iron is made today, however, owing to the quicker methods of producing steel which is free from slag streaks.

Wrought iron is made by refining pig iron in a REVERBERATORY FURNACE, that is, a furnace in which the fire is separate from the metal and the heat is reflected back by means of the shaped roof, Fig. 3. Iron oxide is first sprinkled on the hearth, which is then charged with pig iron. The iron oxide together with the sand on the pig iron forms a slag

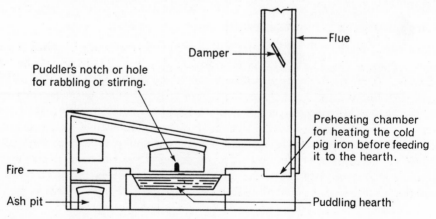

Fig. 3 Puddling furnace

4

which rises to the surface as the charge melts. Oxide scale from the forge shops, known as 'hammer scale' is added and a highly oxidizing slag forms which attacks the impurities in the metal, causing it to bubble and boil.

As the iron becomes purified and refined, its melting point rises and it becomes a spongy mass. The slag is then drawn off by allowing it to run through a hole in the door. The 'boiling' gradually subsides as the carbon is removed and the temperature now raised by opening the damper. Rabbling is continued until the iron is a pasty, spongy mass and in this condition the puddler works it into balls weighing around 36 kg each. These are removed from the furnace one at a time and stacked under a steam hammer, which welds the hot iron into a solid bloom and expels some of the slag during the process. In this state the slag threads are too coarse, so the iron is sheared into short lengths, piled, reheated and again welded into a solid bloom expelling more slag and so producing a cleaner metal. The iron can now be rolled into 'Merchant bar' to give an inferior grade of iron owing to the slag inclusions. If the process of shearing, piling, heating and hammering is repeated, a better metal known as 'Best' is produced; again the process can be repeated to produce 'Best best' and yet again, 'Treble best' which is the highest grade of all. Even so, the slag streaks are still present and can be seen easily with the naked eye.

Steel

At the beginning of the nineteenth century industry was expanding rapidly. The coming of steam pumps to drain the water out of the coal mines enabled deeper mining to be undertaken, while the railways were expanding in their efforts to clear the mounting coal stocks. Machines and engines were also in great demand for the speeding up of production in factories. Clearly there was a growing demand for a good quality iron, free from slag and also strong and cheap. About 1850 Henry Bessemer began experiments in an attempt to solve this problem and in 1856 accidentally produced steel, which is simply iron with carbon in solution.

THE BESSEMER ACID PROCESS

The Bessemer converter, Fig. 4, is a specially shaped cylinder lined with silica bricks or rammed with gannister. It is mounted on trunnions which enable it to rotate by means of hydraulic power. Air blast passes through one of the trunnions to the air box in the base and then into the converter through a nest of tuyeres or air pipes. The converter is first turned horizontally to receive the charge of molten pig iron, the air blast is turned on and the converter rotated to the upright position. A shower of sparks shoots out of the mouth in a continuous stream and a flame gradually appears as the different impurities are burned out of the metal. The oxidizing of the impurities causes a rise in temperature so that no outside heat has to be applied. Carbon is the last to be burned out and the metal becomes agitated. This is known as the boil, and a large white flame appears. Gradually the boil lessens and the flame dies out. The converter is tilted to the first position and the melt is now pure iron.

A weighed quantity of pig iron is added to the molten metal to supply it with carbon, thus turning the iron into steel. This is known as 'killing', because the turbulent metal now becomes calm. As the metal is poured into a ladle, a mixture of silicon and manganese is added to get a metal free from blow holes. From the ladle the metal is teemed into ingots.

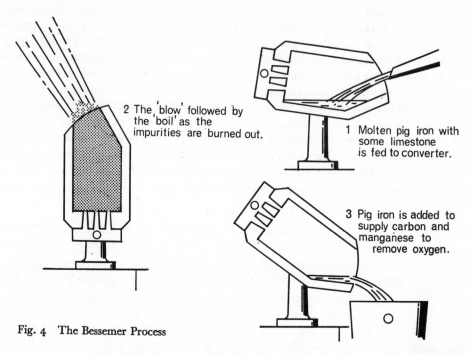

2 The 'blow' followed by the 'boil' as the impurities are burned out.

1 Molten pig iron with some limestone is fed to converter.

3 Pig iron is added to supply carbon and manganese to remove oxygen.

Fig. 4   The Bessemer Process

This method uses hematite iron which is expensive, and efforts to find a method of using cheaper local basic irons resulted in the Bessemer Basic Process. In this, large quantities of lime are required for slag making and this demands a different converter lining. These terms, acid and basic, merely indicate the chemical nature of the lining and the slag used.

The basic process is very similar to the acid in operation except that lime is fed into the converter to form the slag, and after the blow (indicated by the flame dying out) the air is kept on for about four minutes to remove the phosphorous. This is called the after-blow, and is indicated by dense brown fumes billowing out of the converter. The great advantage of the Bessemer process is that no outside heat has to be supplied.

THE OPEN HEARTH PROCESS

After many experiments at fuel economy two German engineers, the Siemens brothers, discovered that preheated air and gas brought about a saving in fuel plus a higher

6

furnace temperature. Owing to the great heat, large furnaces were built and steel added to the charge of pig iron. This was known as the Siemens-Martin process but is now called the Open Hearth Furnace, Fig. 5. As with the Bessemer process, there is both acid and basic according to the hearth lining and the slag.

The open hearth is a large rectangular bath with several charging doors at the front and the tapping hole at the back. The regenerating chambers, consisting of preheated chequered brickwork, are below and heat the air and gas separately. The heated gas and air enter the furnace at one end through two holes side by side, and combustion takes place when they meet, resulting in a large tongue of flame shooting slightly downwards and licking across the surface of the bath. The flame exhausts through two similar holes at the opposite end of the furnace and passes through the regenerator chambers, bringing the chequer patterned brickwork to red heat before finally passing up the chimney.

Every half-hour or so the direction of the flame is reversed by valves so as to maintain the high gas and air temperatures by reheating the regenerator chambers which have been in use. Both oil and producer gas are used as fuel.

The advantages of the Open Hearth method are:

1. Steel scrap can be used with pig iron.

2. The chemical action is slow, therefore better control is possible.

3. The carbon need not all be removed, the process being stopped when the carbon content is right.

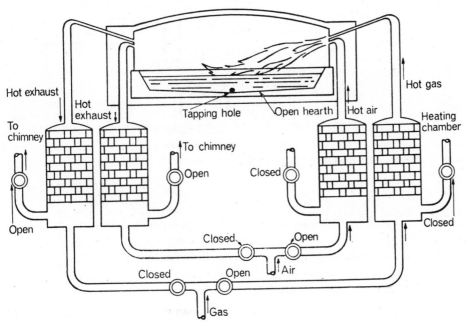

Fig. 5   Open hearth furnace

ELECTRIC FURNACES

A little of the steel produced in this country is made in the electric furnace, of which there are two kinds:

1. The electric arc.
2. The high-frequency induction.

Of the two, the electric arc furnace makes the greater amount of steel. Owing to the lack of a plentiful supply of cheap electricity in this country, the electric furnace has developed slowly. Electric steels are mostly of superior quality, and although the output of these furnaces is small their work is important.

THE ELECTRIC ARC FURNACE

The metal is melted by the large sparks between the metal and the three electrodes, the temperature reaching something like 3500°C. Accurate control is possible in this type of furnace, Fig. 6.

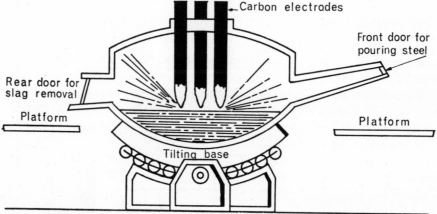

Carbon electrodes

Front door for pouring steel

Rear door for slag removal

Platform

Platform

Tilting base

Fig. 6 Electric arc furnace

THE H.F. INDUCTION FURNACE

The furnace is surrounded by a water-cooled copper pipe the outside of which carries a very high-frequency current which melts the metal. The magnetic action induced in the furnace results in a useful mixing action of the melt, Fig. 7.

Tool steels

Tool steel is simply steel suitable for the making of tools because it contains enough carbon to enable it to be hardened and tempered so that it will be harder than the material it has to cut. Plain tool steel is commonly known as Carbon Steel, while alloy tool steels have small quantities of other metals in them to give faster and better cutting qualities.

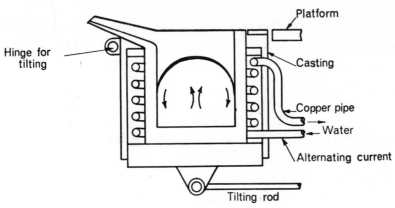

Platform

Hinge for tilting

Casting

Copper pipe

Water

Alternating current

Tilting rod

Fig. 7   H.F. induction furnace

CRUCIBLE CAST STEEL

Once tool steel was made by the cementation process and consisted of sealing bars of Swedish iron in boxes filled with charcoal. These were placed in a furnace and kept at red heat for a week to enable the iron to absorb the carbon, the greatest amount being near the surface. When removed from the furnace the bars were known as Blister Steel because of the small blisters on their surfaces. The bars were cut up and welded together to give a more even distribution of carbon. This metal was called Single Shear Steel because of its popular use for sheep shears in the great sheep days of olden times in Britain. Further cutting and welding gave a better steel known as Double Shear, but even so the uneven quality made it unsuitable for exacting work. The obvious solution

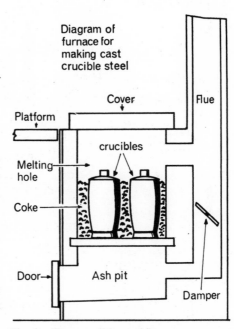

Diagram of furnace for making cast crucible steel

Cover   Flue

Platform

crucibles

Melting hole

Coke

Door→   Ash pit

Damper

Fig. 8   Cast crucible steel furnace

was to melt the steel and get a thorough mixture, but the problem was to find a material which would hold the molten steel at such a high temperature. A Doncaster watchmaker, Benjamin Huntsman, eventually solved the problem about 1740 by making a crucible which remained strong enough when heated. The crucible, or pot, is placed in a small coke-fired furnace and charged with iron and charcoal, Fig. 8. When the metal melts it is poured into long moulds. Steel thus made is known as crucible cast steel and is refined by

9

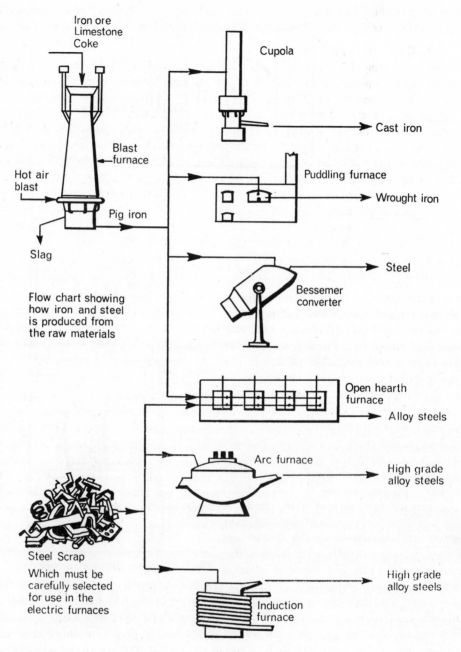

Iron ore
Limestone
Coke

Cupola

Cast iron

Blast
furnace

Hot air
blast

Puddling furnace

Wrought iron

Pig iron

Slag

Steel

Bessemer
converter

Flow chart showing
how iron and steel
is produced from
the raw materials

Open hearth
furnace

Alloy steels

Arc furnace

High grade
alloy steels

Steel Scrap
Which must be
carefully selected
for use in the
electric furnaces

Induction
furnace

High grade
alloy steels

Fig. 9

hammering, rolling and drawing to shape. Although the steel is free from slag, the electric furnace will supersede both the cementation and crucible methods eventually.

ALLOY TOOL STEELS

Before 1871 cutting tools were of plain carbon steel which had to be constantly re-hardened and tempered in cold water with a fairly high failure rate due to cracking and distortion of the tool. Robert Mushet discovered that a manganese tungsten steel could be air-hardened and so opened up a new era in tool manufacture. Not only was this a more satisfactory method of heat treatment, but the tools made from this alloy lasted longer and could cut faster than the old type, thus enabling the development of mass production methods. Since that time research has gone on continuously to improve tool steels, so necessary with the introduction of harder metals in this Space Age.

High-speed steel, known as H.S.S., is one alloy which can stand up to high cutting speeds. The proportions of the alloying elements vary from one manufacturer to another, but a popular composition of H.S.S. is: 18 per cent tungsten, 4 per cent chromium, and 1 per cent vanadium, in a steel containing 0.75 per cent carbon.

BRIGHT DRAWN MILD STEEL

Mild steel ingots at red heat are rolled and drawn through dies, step by step, to reduce them to sheet, strip and bar, the end-product being covered with a hard oxide scale. In this form the metal is known as Black Steel. By pickling to remove this scale and cold drawing the metal through dies for the final stage a clean bright surface results, the metal now being known as Bright Drawn Mild Steel or B.D.M.S. Fig. 9 shows the production of iron and steel in flow chart form.

NEW PROCESSES

Bessemer steel is unsatisfactory for certain work because it contains nitrogen picked up from the air blast. Today, oxygen can be made easily and cheaply in large quantities—called tonnage oxygen—and so a better quality Bessemer steel can be produced. Further-more, new methods of steel manufacture have been developed, such as the LD process. This has become a world's classic and is being adopted by a number of British companies.

The LD process is named after the Austrian towns of LINZ and DONAWITZ where it was first developed. A Bessemer converter is used, but instead of air being blown in through the base, a tube called a lance is lowered into the converter mouth so as to blow a mixture of steam and oxygen on to the metal surface. Scrap metal is used as a coolant.

The advantages of this method are:—
1. Scrap metal is used
2. The speed of manufacture and low cost is similar to the Bessemer process.
3. The final product is as good as open hearth steel.

Two other methods of oxygen steel making are, KALDO and ROTOR.

Once again the phosphorus content of the iron created problems which have been overcome by injecting powdered lime with the oxygen and slagging the metal in two stages.

11

2

The Heat Treatment of Plain Steels

Pure iron consists of crystals or grains of iron called FERRITE which are soft and weak. The addition of a little carbon produces steel consisting of grains of ferrite mixed with hard dark grains of PEARLITE, while 0.9 per cent carbon results in a steel consisting completely of pearlite.

When steels are heated above red heat these grains change into a new structure called AUSTENITE caused by the carbon dissolving, the time for this change varying according to the carbon content. The period during which this change takes place is known as the CRITICAL RANGE, the start and finish being the CRITICAL POINTS, Fig. 10. If the steel is allowed to cool out slowly, it will change back to its original crystal structure, but if suddenly quenched, the austenite is transformed into a hard, needle-like material called MARTENSITE, Fig. 11.

Heating steel beyond the critical range causes the grain size to increase, making a coarse and brittle metal, so heating must always be carefully controlled, Fig. 12. It is important to remember this when working at the forge.

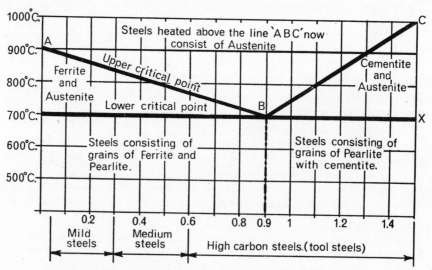

For annealing or hardening, the steel must be heated to just above the line 'A.B.X.'.

Fig. 10

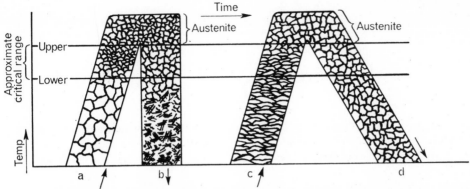

Fig. 11 Steel heated to just above the critical temperature causes a fine grain to develop.

Quenched so as to rapidly cool the steel, results in a hard needle-like structure called 'Martensite'. In mild steels the hardness is slight but in high carbon steels it is great enough to provide cutting tools.

Steel which has been cold worked has deformed grain and must be heated to just above its upper critical temperature to refine it.

By letting it cool out slowly the grain reforms to its original size and shape. This is called the annealed state.

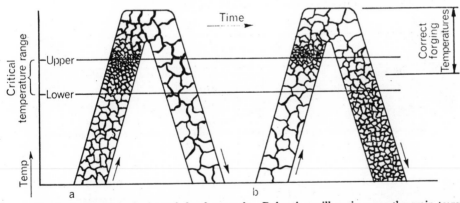

Fig. 12 Steel of normal grain heated for forgework. Above the upper critical temperature the grain grows coarse. If the metal is allowed to cool slowly the coarse grain remains.

Reheating will again cause the grain to refine in the critical temperature range but grow coarse above. Hammering will refine the grain and must be continued to the upper critical temperature to prevent it growing coarse. Hammering below this temperature will have a similar effect to cold working, i.e. harden and distort.

Forging   Steel, 0.1% carbon—900°C.-1300°C.
Temperatures   Steel, 1.5% carbon—800°C.-1050°C.

13

ANNEALING

Annealing means to soften. This has to be done to metal after it has been cold worked such as by hammering and rolling, during which the granular structure is deformed and stresses have developed. Consequently the metal becomes hard and less ductile so that further working will cause it to crack. Steels having up to 0.9 per cent carbon are annealed by heating to just above the upper critical point and then leaving them to cool out slowly in the hearth, the slower the better. The annealed metal is now in its softest state, and has no internal stresses. For steel having more than 0.9 per cent carbon, the annealing temperature is just above the lower critical point, because later heat treatment with this type of steel may cause cracking.

NORMALIZING

This is a form of annealing, but whereas in annealing the metal is brought to its softest state, in normalizing this is not so. It must be realized that certain structural parts, fittings and forgings, if annealed, would be rendered too soft for use. To normalize a piece of steel, it is heated to just above the upper critical point and then allowed to cool freely in still air.

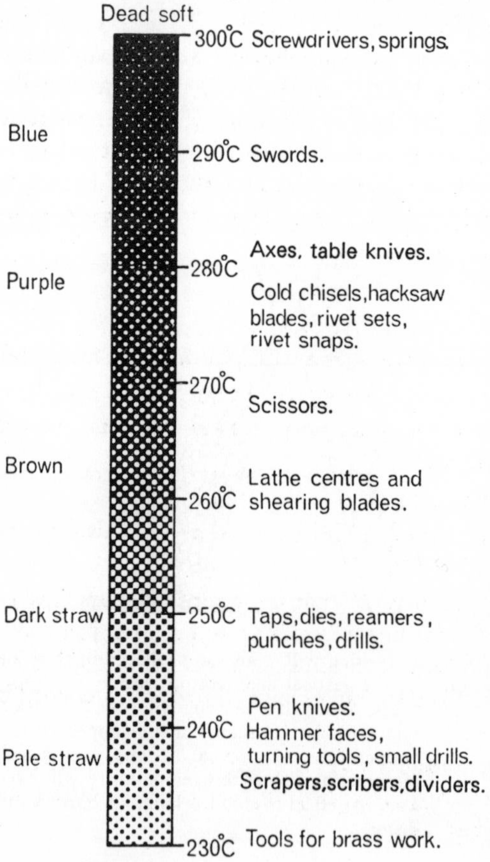

HARDENING

To make a piece of steel hard it should be heated up to its annealing temperature, which is about cherry red heat for carbon steels, so that its structure consists entirely of austenite. Time should be allowed for the heat to soak right through the metal to its middle. In this condition it is quenched in cold water or oil, causing the structure to change into martensite.

TEMPERING

This is a process whereby a hardened piece of steel is made tougher so that it can be used without breaking. Heat is applied gently to the hardened metal until it reaches a temperature between 230°C. and 300°C., the exact temperature depending upon the purpose of the tool or article, Fig. 13. The lower temperature range produces qualities of low shock resistance and a high degree of hardness, while the upper temperature range results in good

Dead soft
Blue
Purple
Brown
Dark straw
Pale straw
Glass hard

- 300°C Screwdrivers, springs.
- 290°C Swords.
- 280°C Axes, table knives. Cold chisels, hacksaw blades, rivet sets, rivet snaps.
- 270°C Scissors.
- 260°C Lathe centres and shearing blades.
- 250°C Taps, dies, reamers, punches, drills.
- 240°C Pen knives. Hammer faces, turning tools, small drills. Scrapers, scribers, dividers.
- 230°C Tools for brass work.

Fig. 13   Temper colour chart

shock resistance and less hardness. At the correct heat, the metal is quenched rapidly by swirling about in the liquid. Hardening and tempering can either be (a) all over, or (b) point. In the former, the whole of the work is hardened and tempered, while in the latter, only the point or cutting edge is hardened and tempered.

EXAMPLES IN HARDENING AND TEMPERING

1. *To harden and temper all over a piece of carbon steel, 25 mm by 18 mm by 6 mm, for use, say, as a cutter.*

(a) Raise the work slowly to a cherry red heat.

(b) Maintain this heat for a few moments to ensure an even heat throughout.

(c) Quench in clean cold water.

(d) Remove from the water trough and polish up the now glass-hard metal using emery cloth. This has to be done so that the temper colours can be seen.

(e) Hold the work over, or place it on, a heated block of steel, moving it about and turning it over occasionally until the required temperature is reached. This is indicated by coloured oxide films, caused by the oxygen in the air attacking the metal as it begins to warm up. This is probably the only time when the formation of oxide films on metal is welcome and serves a useful purpose. The first colour to appear is pale straw, followed by dark straw, then various shades of brown to purple and finally blue, when the metal is now quite hot. When the work shows the required colour it is quenched in clean cold water.

2. *To point harden and temper a cold chisel.*

(a) Heat the cutting end 50 to 60 mm to a cherry red heat.

(b) Maintain this heat for a few moments to ensure even heating throughout the metal.

(c) Quench the end 20 mm only by dipping it in clean cold water. Move it up and down in the water slowly to avoid a sharp boundary between the hard and the soft parts which would cause breakage when in use.

(d) When the chisel end is cooled, withdraw it from the water.

(e) Rub the end 70 mm with a piece of carborundum stone so as to polish up the metal.

(f) Hold the chisel at a suitable angle to the light so that the temper colours may be seen. There should be a small patch of black heat remaining in the chisel just above the part which was immersed. It is from this heat that the temper colours will flow. When the colour purple reaches 3 mm from the chisel edge, the tool is quenched in cold water.

The shank and head must be left in the softened state because the tool is subject to continuous shocks from the hammer when in use. A simpler method is to break the previous operation into two distinct processes, Fig. 14.

(a) Heat the end as before but quench completely in clean cold water.

(b) Clean up the glass h d end of the chisel to get a bright clean surface.

(c) Apply a small flame about 30 to 40 mm from the edge and watch for the temper colours to flow.

(d) When these are seen to travel along the chisel, remove the flame. This will cause the oxide films to slow down and spread out so that the correct colour can be seen more easily and quenching carried out at the right moment.

(e) As soon as the colour purple reaches 3 mm from the edge, quench vertically in cold water.

CASEHARDENING

This means the hardening of the surface skin of a piece of metal and is carried out chiefly on alloy and mild steels. The process provides a hard wearing surface or case of carbon steel around a soft, ductile core. Bolts, pins, gear-wheel teeth, rollers and small pulleys are examples of parts which benefit from casehardening. The method is as follows:

The parts to be casehardened are packed in airtight steel boxes together with material rich in carbon such as charcoal, bone dust and charred leather, or some prepared commercial mixture. They are now heated in a furnace to a temperature of 900°C., so that the red hot steel can absorb carbon from the preparation in which it is packed, this stage often being referred to as 'carburizing'. Heating is maintained for about six hours when the surface of the work will have absorbed carbon to a depth of about 0.8 mm, thus converting this part into carbon steel. A thicker case would require a considerable heating time, the slight extra depth making the effort uneconomical.

The boxes are allowed to cool out slowly and the work is removed. Unfortunately, the long period of heating at a high temperature results in a coarse grain structure in the metal core. This is refined by heating the work to about 850°C. and quenching in water, after which it is heated to about 750°C. and again quenched to refine and harden the high carbon steel case. Finally, the case is tempered.

SURFACE HARDENING

A quick method of hardening the surface of small items such as washers, pins, bolts and small spanner jaws may be carried out in the workshop quite easily, using the forge fire and a proprietory brand of carbon-rich powder. The work is heated to a bright red heat and rolled around in the powder which sticks to the metal and melts on to it. The work is then returned to a clean part of the fire and again brought to a red heat so that carburizing takes place. It is usual to repeat the process of heating and carburizing two or three times before finally quenching so as to form a reliable depth of hardness which seldom exceeds 0.4 mm by this method. Although often spoken of as casehardening, this method is really surface hardening.

ANNEALING NON-FERROUS METALS

ALUMINIUM. Because of the low melting point, 655°C., aluminium should be rubbed with ordinary soap and heated until the soap turns black. This indicates the correct

1 Heat the end 50 mm to a cherry red heat. Keep flame off end to avoid overheating.

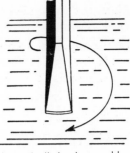

2. Quench vertically in clean cold water. Swirl round. The end is now glass hard.

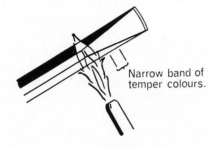

Narrow band of temper colours.

3 Clean the end 70 mm bright using emery cloth. Apply a small flame to the tool about 40 mm from the end and when the temper colours appear, remove the flame. This will cause the moving band of temper colours to slow down.

straw
light brown
brown
purple
blue

4 The temper colours will now spread towards the cutting edge more slowly.

5. When the colour purple reaches 3 mm from the edge, quench vertically in clean cold water. Swirl round.

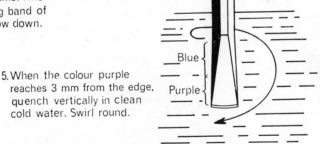

Blue
Purple

Fig. 14 Hardening and tempering

annealing temperature, 400°C., and the metal should now be quenched in water or can be left to cool slowly.

COPPER. Support the metal on its edges to prevent heat loss to the firebricks. Raise to a dull red heat then quench in water or leave to cool out slowly.

BRASS. Raise to a very dull red heat then leave to cool out slowly.

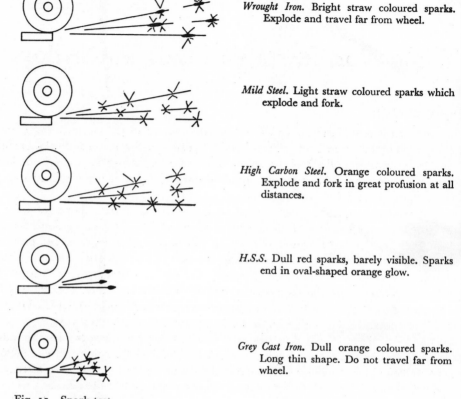

Wrought Iron. Bright straw coloured sparks. Explode and travel far from wheel.

Mild Steel. Light straw coloured sparks which explode and fork.

High Carbon Steel. Orange coloured sparks. Explode and fork in great profusion at all distances.

H.S.S. Dull red sparks, barely visible. Sparks end in oval-shaped orange glow.

Grey Cast Iron. Dull orange coloured sparks. Long thin shape. Do not travel far from wheel.

Fig. 15   Spark test

Identification of ferrous metals

It is sometimes necessary to identify a piece of ferrous metal in the workshop. If a short length is sawn off the metal under inspection, heated and quenched in water, it is possible to determine whether the metal is tool steel or not from the resultant degree of hardness. A quick method is the spark test which enables identification of the metal to be made from the size, shape and colour of the spark produced at the grindstone, Fig. 15.

If the metal is of a size which can be bent by hammering in the bench vice, some idea of its identity can be got from the amount of bending the metal can take before cracking. Wrought iron can be bent back on itself while mild steel can take a good bend. Carbon steel will bend very little before snapping.

Another method is to hacksaw nearly through the metal and then snap the piece off. An inspection of the fractured end will give a clue as to the type of metal it is. A fibrous break denotes wrought iron, while a silvery crystalline fracture is given by mild steel. A very close grained pale grey fracture denotes carbon steel.

3

Some Non-ferrous Metals and Alloys

ALUMINIUM

Aluminium is one of the most plentiful of the elements in the world, being found as a compound in rocks and most clays. A hundred years ago it was rare and valuable because only very small quantities of the metal had been separated from the ore. In fact, the Emperor Napoleon III had an aluminium dinner service which was valued and prized more than one of gold.

The principal ore from which aluminium is obtained is Bauxite, named after Les Baux in southern France, where the ore was first discovered. The ore contains many impurities, including iron, and needs purifying. To do this, it is crushed, roasted and ground to a powder and then fed into pressurized chambers containing heated caustic soda solution which causes the aluminium oxide to separate from the insoluble material. The aluminate solution is pumped into tanks where crystals form as the saturated solution cools.

These crystals are then heated in long revolving drums, thus driving off the water in combination and leaving aluminium oxide, or alumina. During this roasting process the crystals crumble to form a white powder which, when cool, is ready for the reduction works. Here the powdered alumina is mixed in a bath with molten cryolite (a mineral obtainable only from Greenland) which causes it to melt. By passing an electric current through the furnace lining sufficient heat is generated to melt the cryolite and the passage of the current decomposes the alumina into two parts:

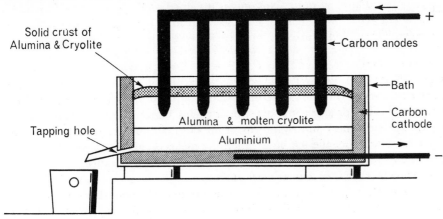

Fig. 16   Aluminium furnace

1. Metallic, which is the aluminium and collects at the bottom of the bath.

2. Non-metallic, which collects at the rods (the anodes) and burns away.

The cryolite is unaffected by the chemical action. The alumina is added at frequent intervals and the furnaces tapped regularly to draw off the aluminium. This chemical action which is required to break down, or decompose, the alumina is called electrolysis and the liquid in the bath is known as the electrolyte, Fig. 16.

For efficient production, great quantities of cheap electricity must be available, consequently alumina reduction works are built near waterfalls or where artificial falls can be made. Some of the properties which make aluminium second only to steel in popularity are:

1. Low weight combined with strength.

2. Resistance to corrosion.

3. Good electrical and thermal conductivity.

4. Its compounds are non-poisonous.

Like many metals in the pure state, aluminium has a limited usefulness, being soft and weak. Alloyed with a small amount of other metals, however, its range of work becomes considerable. The alloying elements commonly added are: copper, magnesium, manganese, silicon, nickel and zinc.

COPPER

Copper was one of the first metals known to man and is believed to have been named after the island where it was first discovered—Cyprus. It is the only pink coloured metal and is valued for its importance in electrical work. Copper is very malleable and ductile and possesses high electrical and thermal properties, being second only to silver in that respect. It can be rolled into foil 0.1 mm thick, and drawn into wire having a uniform diameter of less than 0.02 mm. Not only is it valued as a metal in itself, but also as an alloying agent with other metals such as zinc and tin, making brass and bronze respectively. The manufacture of copper is carried out in two distinct stages:

1. The making of blister copper.

2. Refining blister copper by fire or electrolysis.

The roasted ore or 'calcine', containing many impurities, is charged into a reverberatory furnace which produces molten 'matte'. This matte is charged into a converter similar to the Bessemer, and by means of air blast, impurities are oxidized from the metal. The blow lasts some ten hours, then the metal is cast into cakes. As it cools, the surface of the metal becomes uneven and blistered in appearance, consequently the metal is known as, 'blister copper'.

This crude blister copper is refined by remelting in a reverberatory furnace and blowing air in to oxidize the impurities. Slag is removed next from the surface of the liquid which is then covered with coal, coke or other carbon-rich materials and 'green' poles and tree trunks are pushed beneath the surface, releasing gases which lower the oxygen content of the copper. When this figure reaches 0.30 to 0.05 per cent the metal is cast and is known as Tough Pitch Copper.

This copper contains impurities such as gold and silver, so for greater purity it pays to refine by electrolysis.

The three main types of copper used in engineering are:

1. High Conductivity or H.C. Copper. This has the highest purity being 99.9 per cent or more copper. It is used extensively for electrical and thermal purposes.

2. Refined Tough Pitch Copper. This contains metallic and other impurities, it is good but not quite up to the standard of H.C. copper.

3. Arsenical Copper. This contains up to about 0.5 per cent arsenic, which improves the strength and toughness but it is not used for electrical gear.

TIN

Tin has a silvery white lustrous appearance and when a piece of pure tin is bent it emits a peculiar sound called the 'cry of tin'. It has been known since earliest times and the Phoenicians sailed all the way to Cornwall to trade their famous purple cloth for supplies of it. Because tin is unaffected by acids from foodstuffs, the greatest use of tin is in the making of tinplate for the food canning industry. Other important uses of tin are for the making of alloys such as bronze, Babbitt metal, and soft solders.

Tin occurs chiefly in the ores tinstone and cassiterite and is easily reduced, after which it must be refined before use.

ZINC

Zinc is a bluish white brittle metal and has a strong resistance to corrosion. The metal was known in prehistoric times chiefly for its use in the making of brass, though zinc ornaments have been discovered. The discovery that iron and steel coated with a thin layer of zinc gave protection from rust for long periods caused a big demand for the metal.

Corrosion is an electrical process, and as the zinc is in contact with the steel, the zinc weathers away rather than the steel. Thus, because it is an electrical action, metals which have been coated with zinc are said to be 'galvanized'.

To galvanize, the iron or steel objects are first dipped in hot dilute acid to clean off dirt and scale. This is followed by immersion in a flux and finally a bath of molten zinc. Sometimes a little tin is added to the zinc dip, causing a peculiar pattern to form not unlike frosting. Electroplating is also used and gives a controlled depth of coat. A new process called sherardizing has been developed and uses zinc powder which is baked on the metal at about 300°C. Today the most important uses of zinc are in the manufacture of brass, and as a protective coating on iron and steel. As zinc sulphide it is essential in the making of fluorescent screens for television.

The ores, sphalerite or blend, are concentrated and roasted in air to remove most of the sulphur which is led away and made into sulphuric acid. Zinc is then obtained from the concentrate by (a) thermal reduction, or (b) electrolytic extraction.

LEAD

Lead is a soft heavy metal with a bluish-grey colour. The Romans worked the English lead mines during their period of occupation, and examples of the use they made of the metal are still to be seen in the water pipes and tanks at Bath.

Pure lead is used extensively for electric cable covering, chemical tank linings and electric storage batteries.

Lead is obtained from the ore galena and often contains some silver. The extraction is quite simple, the ore being first roasted to burn away the sulphur, then smelted in a blast furnace.

ALLOYS

Two or more metals when mixed together produce an alloy having completely different characteristics from the metals used to make it. Qualities such as strength, colour, hardness and melting point usually vary considerably. For this reason the alloying of metals is important as it enables us to make new 'metals' to meet the ever-growing demands of progress, instead of being restricted to the limitations of the few basic metals provided by nature. In addition, three non-metallic elements, CARBON, PHOSPHOROUS and SILICON, behave in alloys as though they were metals and impart particular qualities where required.

The first known alloy was bronze, no doubt accidentally made and discovered when smelting copper. It was found that bronze was harder than copper and therefore a better material for tools and weapons. Bronze generally consists of 96 per cent copper and 4 per cent tin, but the proportions may vary according to particular needs—church bells, for instance, demanding an alloy of 94 per cent copper and 6 per cent tin to produce a pleasing tone. Today, our pennies and halfpennies are made from a bronze alloy of 97 per cent copper, 0.5 per cent tin and 2.5 per cent zinc which has good wearing qualities. Consequently these coins are much lighter and thinner than those minted before 1860, which were of pure copper.

An alloy of copper and zinc gives us the useful metal brass, which varies in colour and strength according to the mixture. Brass is ideal for use in marine work as it stands up excellently to the effects of both ordinary water and sea water.

Five kinds of brass in common use are:

Gilding Metal (88 per cent copper, 12 per cent zinc)

Cartridge Brass (70 per cent copper, 30 per cent zinc)

English Standard Brass (66 per cent Copper, 34 per cent zinc)

Basis or Common Brass (63 per cent copper, 37 per cent zinc)

Muntz Metal, Yellow Metal, or Drill Rod (60 per cent copper, 40 per cent zinc)

Brass can be very difficult to cut unless new, or newly sharpened tools are employed.

To make cutting easier it is usual to mix a small percentage of lead with the alloy, and this lead, scattered throughout the brass, has no other effect on the metal except, unfortunately, to make it 'hot short'. That is, when this brass is hot it is brittle and should not be moved about or worked until it is cold.

Pure aluminium is too soft for the engineer but may be used for domestic and ornamental work. When alloyed with a small quantity of copper, its strength is greatly increased without seriously affecting its weight and it has become an important metal in the aircraft industry.

When tin and lead are alloyed they produce soft solder, more lead giving a coarse solder suitable for outdoor use, while more tin produces a finer solder suitable for small intricate work, especially where good flowing qualities are needed. A little bismuth added to soft solders improves the flowing quality as well as lowering the melting point, while antimony added to the alloy not only lowers the melting point, but in addition gives a harder solder and causes slight expansion on cooling. This unusual property of expanding while cooling which is possessed by antimony is made use of in type metal, to give clear and distinct printing.

Hard solders are alloys of copper, zinc and silver in varying proportions to give different melting points as well as other qualities. Probably the lowest melting point alloy of all is that having a composition of 50 per cent bismuth, 25 per cent lead, $12\frac{1}{2}$ per cent tin, and $12\frac{1}{2}$ per cent cadmium, and which melts at a temperature of 60°C. It is known as Wood's Alloy and is used particularly in scientific work such as in the sealing of glass in the making of air- and vacuum-tight boxes. Another important use is as a safety plug in ceiling sprinklers in large department stores and warehouses. Tungsten, a rare heavy white metal, gives steel hardness and a fine grain and also enables it to withstand great heat. Tools made from this steel cut faster and quicker than the plain carbon steel tools. Magnets are made from tungsten steel because it holds magnetism. Chromium is a very hard metal used in the making of stainless and high-tensile steels. It is a bluish white metal and added to steel imparts strength and toughness to the alloy, which is able to resist rust and heavy blows.

Chromium steel is used where heavy duty is needed, such as in car engine valves. Nickel adds strength, toughness and elasticity to steel and is used for railway axles and special rails such as crossings and points as well as armour plating.

Main bearings of engines are lined with a soft alloy called White Metal because of its colour. Sometimes known as Babbitt Metal, it consists of tin with a little copper and antimony, and is ideal for high speed engines. Being soft, the alloy beds itself to the shaft without damaging it. The bearing must of course, be well lubricated.

SOME PROPERTIES OF METALS

Compressive strength is the resistance to being crushed.

Shear strength is the resistance to breaking sideways.

Tenacity is the resistance to being pulled apart.

Brittleness is the ability to break easily.

Ductility is the ability to be drawn out long and fine.

Elasticity is the ability to reform to the original shape after deformation.

Hardness is the resistance to cutting.

Malleability is the ability to be thinned and spread over a larger area by hammering or rolling.

Toughness is the resistance to breaking.

4

Safety Precautions in Workshops

The tools and equipment in a workshop can be good servants but terrible masters, and although it is unlikely that accidents can be completely eliminated, a little thought and care can reduce them to negligible proportions.

The worker should have his jacket off, shirt sleeves rolled up to the elbow, and an apron should be worn—being dressed for the part, he works better. Hair styles must be watched because of rotating spindles.

Movement about the room should be at walking pace, tools being carried pointing downwards. Switches and machines ought never to be interfered with unless instruction and permission have been given to the worker. Never talk to anyone engaged on a machine, his attention must be completely on his work.

When working at the forge, heat and fire are the two biggest dangers. Leave nothing inflammable lying about in the area of the forge. After use, the tongs should always be quenched in water before returning them to their rack. The anvil should be close to the fire to reduce the distance through which hot metal is carried, and no more than two people should work at the forge at one time. It is a good habit to wet one's fingers and touch metal quickly to avoid burns.

At the drilling machine all work must be securely held in a vice or by means of clamps, and a small paint brush used for the removal of swarf which is razor sharp. The operator should stand in front of the machine and understand how to start and stop it.

At the buffing spindle, work should be held in the hands and not by means of cloth, rags or the operator's apron.

On the power hacksaw, work must be securely held and long lengths properly supported. Never reach across any machine. The bench shears demands concentration and only one person at a time should use it. All waste cuttings should be removed to the scrap bin. Soldering benches should be kept clean. Many fluxes are corrosive and care must be exercised in handling and working with them.

At the lathe, work and tool must have minimum overhang, and the 'set-up' should be checked at least twice before attempting to operate the machine.

File tangs are dangerous: always fit a wooden handle. No files should be used on lathework. Return all accessories to a special rack or cupboard provided, especially chuck keys, which must never be left in the chuck. Lathe ways and the headstock must at all times be kept clear of drawings and tools.

Metal should be placed in the vice so that it does not project in gangways or aisles. Chipping is a problem at times and care must be taken to ensure the safety of other people in the vicinity. It is advisable to use goggles and place a metal screen in front of the vice and warn others, so as to reduce the risk of injury to nearby workers from flying metal.

A pleasant attitude, a calm manner, a lot of common sense and a willingness to do as one is told, go a long way towards complete safety in the workshop.

Vices

USE. Vices are used for gripping work firmly, the commonest type being that bolted to the work bench and called the Bench or Fitters' vice.

BENCH OR FITTERS' VICE, Fig. 17.

PARTS. 1. Moving jaw, cast iron.
2. Fixed jaw, cast iron.
3. Jaw plates, carbon steel, hardened and tempered.
4. Handle, mild steel.
5. Screwed spindle, mild steel.

In use, cast iron must be handled with care owing to its brittle nature, though quite often it is treated to make it slightly malleable. The jaw plates have diamond-shaped teeth which aid gripping but mark the material being held. For heavy tools this does not matter because the important thing is to obtain a secure grip, but for articles of work, vice marks can be damaging and unsightly.

To protect the work the jaw plates must be covered with pieces of soft metal, wood, or

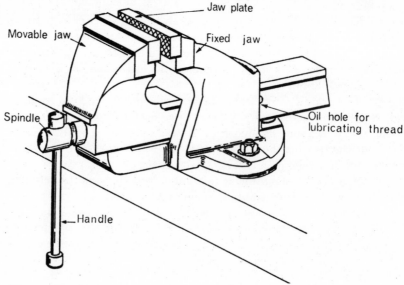

Fig. 17 Bench vice

fibre called vice clamps. The most satisfactory vice clamps are made from lead at least 6 mm thick, but this is very expensive and mild steel will serve quite well, though folded paper must be added for extra protection when working in the softer metals such as copper, brass and aluminium.

In this type of vice the jaw faces are parallel and consequently can grip with the same efficiency when opened at any position. The vice is obtainable in many sizes denoted by the length of the jaw plates in mm.

THE SMITHS' OR LEG VICE, Fig. 18

PARTS. 1. Fixed jaw and leg, wrought iron or mild steel.

2. Moving jaw, wrought iron or mild steel.

3. Spindle, handle, nut box, wrought iron or mild steel.

4. Strap, plate, gib and cotter, mild steel.

5. Spring, carbon steel.

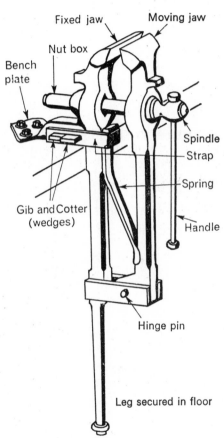

Fig. 18 Leg vice

This is an older type of vice, gradually disappearing in favour of the bench vice. For heavy work and holding hot metal, however, it is unequalled, having a sturdy construction which can withstand considerable rough usage.

Because the moving jaw swings through an arc, the jaws are parallel in only one position, with the result that gripping is not as secure and safe as with the bench vice; in fact, the gripping of round bar horizontally can be dangerous. As with all vices which are fixed to the bench, the top of the vice jaws should reach the elbow or slightly above for comfortable working.

HAND VICE, Fig. 19

Used for holding small work, sheet and strip metal. This is a popular vice for use at the bench or drilling machine.

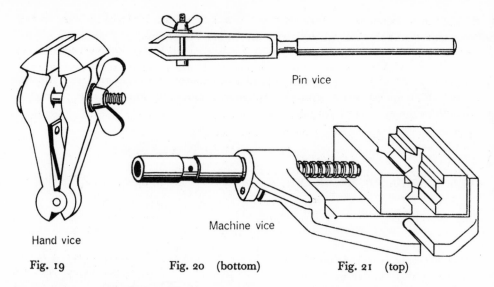

Pin vice

Machine vice

Hand vice

Fig. 19   Fig. 20   (bottom)   Fig. 21   (top)

MACHINE VICE, Fig. 20

These are many and varied and are used for gripping work which has to be machined by one process or another, such as shaping, drilling or milling. The jaws are ground true and flat in the best quality for accurate work, and the body may be adjustable for rotating through any number of degrees.

PIN VICE, Fig. 21

Used for holding very small work. Both the hand and pin vice may be held in the bench vice when both hands are needed or when extra rigidity is required.

Files

Files are used for cutting and smoothing metal and are made from plain carbon steel containing 1.3 per cent carbon.

To avoid breakage in use, the tangs are tempered to remove brittleness by immersing them in a bath of molten lead. This anneals the tangs without affecting the hardened blades.

TEETH

These are formed so that the file cuts on the forward stroke only. If only one series of cuts is made across the blade, the teeth are shaped like knife blades and the file is known as a SINGLE CUT, often called a FLOAT, Fig. 22. This type of file is essential for the softer metals such as wrought iron, copper and aluminium which tend to stick in the file teeth.

If a second series of cuts is made at an angle to the first, thus forming diamond-shaped teeth, the file is known as a DOUBLE CUT and is of general use for medium hard metals. Softer metals choke double cut teeth and render the file useless.

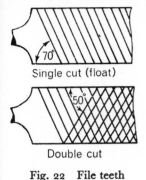

Single cut (float)

Double cut

Fig. 22   File teeth

The cut of a file is known by the number of teeth per 25 mm and is in proportion to the blade length but consideration is being given to the idea of grading double cut files by the density of teeth per given area. Cuts vary slightly from one manufacturer to another, but the following is representative for a 250 mm file:

File	No. of Teeth per 25 mm	
Rough cut	16	
Bastard cut	26	These three cuts
Second cut	36	are in more
Smooth cut	60	general use
Dead smooth cut	100	

The shape of a file is determined by the cross-section of the blade and a few common shapes are: flat, half-round, round, square, three square, Fig. 23. All these files are tapered towards the blade end for about one-third of their length. They have teeth on both sides and edges.

Hand   Flat   Half round   Round   Square   Three square

Fig. 23   Some file sections

There is one file which does not fit into this category. Although flat in cross-section, it tapers in thickness, has parallel sides and one 'safe' edge, that is, an edge without any teeth on it, and is particularly useful for filing stepped work and corners where vertical edges must not be touched. This tool is called a HAND FILE, probably because it was once known as a 'handy' file, Fig. 24.

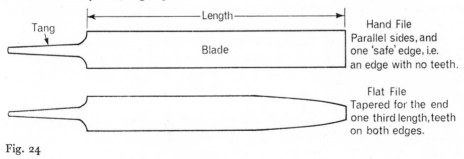

Tang

Length

Blade

Hand File
Parallel sides, and
one 'safe' edge, i.e.
an edge with no teeth.

Flat File
Tapered for the end
one third length, teeth
on both edges.

Fig. 24

File lengths are measured by the length of the blade and vary from 100 to 400 mm increasing in steps of 50 mm. From 100 to 300 mm are the lengths in general use, but for fine work, Swiss or Needle Files are used, Fig. 25. These are obtainable in two sizes, 14 cm and 16 cm and in a variety of shapes. Their tangs are extended, cylindrical in shape and knurled to serve as handles. Great care is needed when working with these files because they are easily broken.

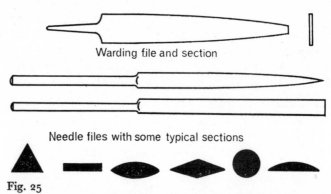

Warding file and section

Needle files with some typical sections

Fig. 25

Warding files are small thin files having a broad blade. They also are useful for small work, especially slot filing, and their broad blade gives them the strength lacking in needle files when using the edge. They are so called because of their use by locksmiths.

Except for needle files, it is vital to fit wooden handles prior to use. The handle is pushed on the tang and tapped firmly in place by knocking the handle base sharply on a solid block. To remove the handle, the file blade is gripped and pulled smartly across the tail of the vice so as to catch the edge of the wooden handle and knock it off.

Brass is a delightful metal to work if we use newly sharpened tools, but it can prove most difficult otherwise. Once a tool has been used on iron or steel, it is useless on brass and will merely slide over it. New files should therefore be used on nothing but brass and should be dabbed with paint for easy identification. They are then known as brass files.

First cuts on any metal with a new file should be light because the fine pointed brittle teeth are easily broken at this stage. Later, as the first sharpness wears down, pressure may be increased. After a period of use on brass and when the files cease to cut efficiently, they can be used for filing steel and a new set of files brought in to use as 'brass files'. When ordering new files or when choosing one for work, three details must be stated: (a) the length, (b) the shape, (c) the cut.

Files will only cut as long as their teeth are in good condition, so treat them with care.

PINNING

Filing eventually causes the file teeth to become choked with small pieces of metal. The file is said to be pinned and causes score marks across the surface of the metal being filed. The file must be cleaned by rubbing a wire brush, called a file card, or a piece of end-grain hardwood, across the blade and following the grooves of the teeth.

After cleaning, a piece of chalk should be rubbed up the blade towards the tang to help reduce or delay pinning.

FILING

For a right-handed person the correct position for filing should be with the left foot pointing forward, the right foot a short pace behind and pointing a little to the right, and a slight crouch with the elbows pointing outwards. The palm of the left hand should press down on the end of the file blade and the right hand should grip firmly the wooden handle attached to the file tang. For light filing, the fingers instead of the palm of the left hand are often used to balance the file.

The direction of filing should always be at an angle to the length of the vice jaws—about 30°—and the file should sweep from end to end of the work with each stroke, using

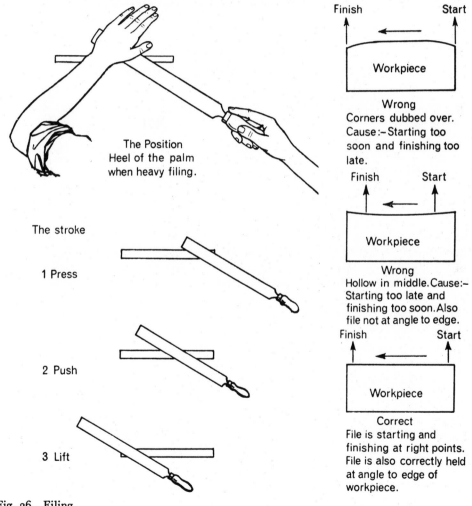

The Position
Heel of the palm
when heavy filing.

The stroke

1 Press

2 Push

3 Lift

Finish   Start

Workpiece

Wrong
Corners dubbed over.
Cause:–Starting too
soon and finishing too
late.

Finish   Start

Workpiece

Wrong
Hollow in middle. Cause:–
Starting too late and
finishing too soon. Also
file not at angle to edge.

Finish   Start

Workpiece

Correct
File is starting and
finishing at right points.
File is also correctly held
at angle to edge of
workpiece.

Fig. 26   Filing

as much of the blade as possible. This means that the balance of the file is constantly varying, and is the cause of most trouble with beginners.

Where much filing has to be done, it is a good plan to change direction and file from the opposite end of the work. A curve is more common than a straight edge during early efforts at filing. This will be cured by regular practice and remembering to, 'PRESS, PUSH and LIFT', during each stroke. Also, by thinking of each file stroke in three parts:

1. the starting point,
2. the file cutting along the metal, and
3. the finishing point.

The point of starting and finishing should be adjusted until a straight edge results, Fig. 26.

The purpose of filing in many cases is to get a straight edge, and this is tested by using a rule, Fig. 27.

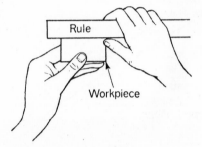

Fig. 27 Testing with rule

Filing should always be finished off by drawfiling. This removes the file marks and produces a smooth finish. The file should be cleaned and lightly rubbed with chalk, then gripped in both hands. The blade is held at right angles to the work and drawn back and forth along the edge—hence the term drawfiling, Fig. 28.

Care must be taken not to overdo drawfiling as it results in hollowing of the work if continued for any length of time.

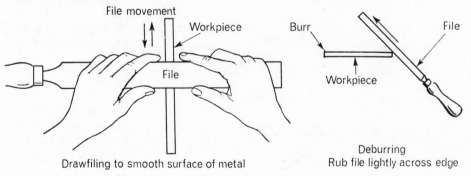

Drawfiling to smooth surface of metal

Deburring
Rub file lightly across edge

Fig. 28

DEBURRING. Having filed the edge correctly, then drawfiled it to remove the file-marks, the ragged edge or burr must be removed by lightly drawfiling the edge at an angle of 45° until the burr peels off, Fig. 28.

When filing, the work should be as low down in the vice as possible to reduce vibration, also the line to which one is filing should be horizontal.

It is much more difficult to file a short edge, say under 25 mm long, than a long edge, but the following method avoids difficulties: Lay the file on the work at about 30° or thereabouts to the edge of the metal, but so that the file blade completely covers the edge. Filing should now proceed by pushing the file forward in the direction of its length only. By holding the file horizontal, a true edge must result if the work is held correctly in the vice.

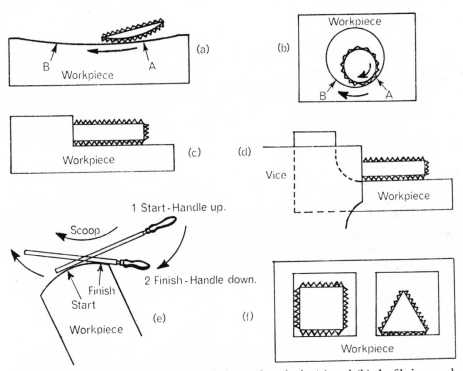

Fig. 29   Filing various shapes.   On each forward stroke in (a) and (b) the file is moved from right to left and given a slight clockwise twist

The filing of other edges is shown in Fig. 29, while Fig. 30 shows the routine for filing metal plate to size and Fig. 31 the method of filing a spigot on the end of a rod.

To save time where a number of similar shapes are required, a metal pattern is made and used for marking out. This pattern is known as a TEMPLATE.

B*

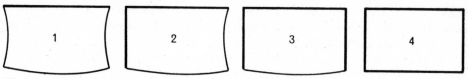

Fig. 30

1. File one long edge straight. Remove as little metal as possible. Test with rule. Drawfile smooth. Further testing and marking out is from this edge known as a reference or datum edge.

2. File one short edge square to the datum edge. Remove as little metal as possible. Test with try square. Drawfile smooth.

3. Measure to length, square line across (rule, try square, scriber). File to line, check with try square. Drawfile smooth.

4. Mark to width (odd leg calipers, rule). File to line, check with calipers. Drawfile smooth. (*Note:* the surface gauge and surface plate could be used to mark to length and width.

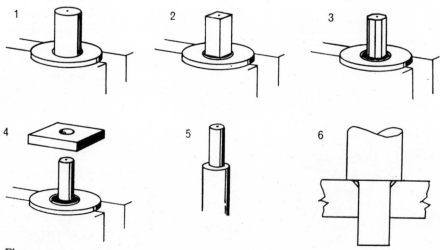

Fig. 31

1 Locate workpiece in vice using a strip of tinplate as vice clamps. Place washer over work with pin length projecting. Pop mark pin end in centre for guidance.

2 File pin to square section. Use hand file with safe edge on washer.

3 File pin to octagonal section.

4 File pin to size. Use a drilled hole as a gauge.

5 Finished pin.

6 Countersink hole slightly to allow for rounded corner at pin base. A tight shoulder joint will result.

5

Scribers, Rivets and Riveting

THE SCRIBER, Fig. 32

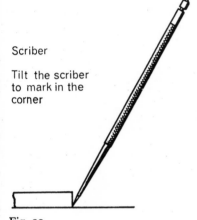

Scriber

Tilt the scriber
to mark in the
corner

Fig. 32

Use. For marking out on metal by scratching the surface.

Material. Carbon steel, point hardened and tempered.

This useful tool is generally used with a rule or try-square for scribing lines when marking out. It is made in a variety of shapes and sizes for various needs. The machinist's scriber is a good plain type and has a knurled shank for ease of holding. The point is ground to an angle of 20° and must be kept sharp.

In use, the scriber point should first be placed on the mark and then the rule or try-square slid along to touch it.

SPRING DIVIDERS, Fig. 33

Use. 1. Stepping off distances.
  2. Measuring the lengths of curves.
  3. Describing arcs and circles.

Parts. 1. Spring, carbon steel, hardened and spring tempered. The spring forces the legs open.
  2. Legs, carbon steel, shaped, then point hardened and tempered.
  3. Pin or fulcrum, steel.
  4. Nut and screw, mild steel. The nut enables the legs to be closed.

Spring dividers are the metalworker's compasses, and can also be considered as a scriber adapted for scribing circles and arcs. A small centre-punch mark is necessary in hard metals to locate one leg and prevent it slipping about. The tool is a light one, easy to handle and useful on small precision work.

A heavier type of dividers is the WING COMPASSES, consisting of two carbon steel legs of

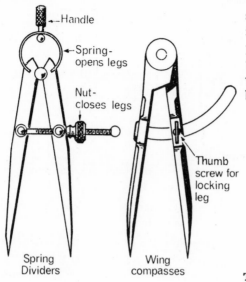

Spring Dividers

Wing compasses

sturdy size connected at one end by a well-fitting bridle joint and rivet. A quadrant plate or wing from one leg curves and passes through a slot in the other leg, which is fitted with a thumb screw to enable the tool to be locked in position at any set size.

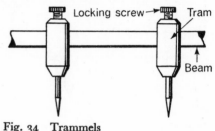

Fig. 34   Trammels

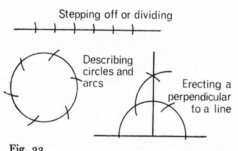

Stepping off or dividing

Describing circles and arcs

Erecting a perpendicular to a line

Fig. 33

TRAMMELS, Fig. 34

Use.   For marking out large arcs and circles beyond the scope of the dividers. Beams are available for work up to 1800 mm radius.

Parts. 1. The beam, made of steel or light alloy and of stout section to ensure rigidity in use.

2. The trams, two in number, with hardened and tempered points.

ODD-LEG CALIPERS, *also known as* JENNY CALIPERS, JENNIES *and* HERMAPHRODITE CALIPERS, Fig. 35

Use.   1. For scribing lines parallel to an edge.
2. For scribing centre lines on metal strip.
3. For marking out the centres of round and square bars.

Parts. 1. Guide leg, carbon steel, point hardened and tempered to resist wear.
2. Scribing leg, may consist of a straight leg of carbon steel ground to a scribing point and point hardened and tempered, or a short leg to which is attached a small scriber by means of a knurled nut and clamp.
3. The joint, consists of a nut and bolt with washer, usually of fibre to ensure a smooth movement.

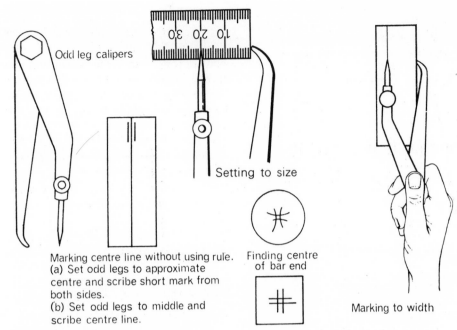

Marking centre line without using rule.
(a) Set odd legs to approximate
centre and scribe short mark from
both sides.
(b) Set odd legs to middle and
scribe centre line.

Finding centre
of bar end

Marking to width

Fig. 35

Adjustable odd-leg calipers are probably better than the plain type, though more expensive, because the scriber legs can be kept in good order more easily and adjusted for correct length quickly and simply. When setting to size the guide leg is hooked on the end of the rule and the calipers opened until the scribing leg point is set to the correct distance.

The use of odd-leg calipers enables repetition work to be carried out without the fatigue of constantly measuring with the rule.

ENGINEERS' HAMMERS, Fig. 36

Use.   For striking with force.

Parts.   1. Head, carbon steel, hardened and tempered.
   2. Handle, haft or shaft. Usually ash because of its springiness, thereby giving maximum force without discomfort to the operator.
   3. Wedges. Hardwood, sometimes steel.

The head varies in weight from 60 g to 900 g, but 225 g is light enough for most delicate work in the general metalwork shop, while 340 g and 450 g is found to cover all bench work of a general nature.

Hammers are made with a rectangular hole rounded at the ends passing right through the middle of the head, and tapering inwards from both sides. This hole is usually

37

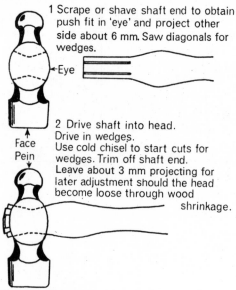

1 Scrape or shave shaft end to obtain push fit in 'eye' and project other side about 6 mm. Saw diagonals for wedges.

←Eye

Face

Pein

2 Drive shaft into head.
Drive in wedges.
Use cold chisel to start cuts for wedges. Trim off shaft end.
Leave about 3 mm projecting for later adjustment should the head become loose through wood shrinkage.

Fig. 36   Hammer

referred to as the 'eye'. The striking face is slightly convex to reduce the tendency to mark the metal being struck and should be kept clean and smooth for best results. In the case of the engineers' hammer, the pein is ball shaped and is useful for spreading down metal, for example, when riveting. The length of the handle provides the leverage and its shape gives added force by virtue of its spring.

When in use the hammer shaft should be gripped near the end or about two-thirds of the way from the head so as to get the best use of the leverage offered, thus making the hammer head really do its work.

CENTRE PUNCH, Fig. 37

Use.   For making cone-shaped dents in metal to guide the nose of the twist drill when drilling.

Material. Carbon steel, point hardened and tempered.

The shape is usually octagonal or hexagonal which not only affords a good grip but also prevents the tool rolling off the bench. If cylindrical in shape, the body is knurled for gripping purposes.

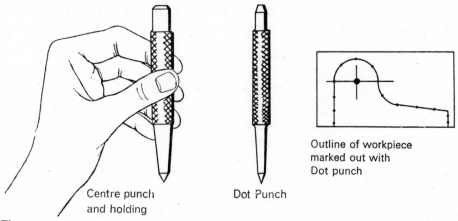

Centre punch and holding

Dot Punch

Outline of workpiece marked out with Dot punch

Fig. 37

When using a centre punch, the metal being worked should be supported on a chipping block or anvil for solid support. The centre punch should be gripped between the thumb and first three fingers which are supported by the little finger resting on the metal. The point is placed on the mark and first lightly struck with a hammer. After examining the 'pop' mark to ensure its accuracy, the mark is enlarged and deepened.

When marking out it is usual lightly to 'pop' mark the outline for clarity. This enables the operator to see more clearly when cutting to a line as all pop marks will be split in two.

The mark made by a centre punch is referred to as a 'pop' mark, probably because of the noise made by the punch when being used. When marking out fine work a lighter form of centre punch is used having a very slender taper and a point ground to about 30°. This tool is used for light marking out only and is known as a DOT or PRICK PUNCH.

RULE, Fig. 38

Use. For testing a straight edge and for measuring.

Material. Carbon steel, hardened and tempered all over to a spring temper.

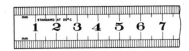

Fig. 38   Rule

Reading of a rule is made easier by rubbing chalk over the surface and wiping clean thus causing the markings to show up white. The 300 mm rule is general and popular for most work, though the 150 mm rule is handy for small work in awkward places as well as for jobs in the lathe.

ENGINEERS' SQUARE, Fig. 39

Use. For testing two straight edges which meet at 90°, for marking out lines at right angles to an edge, and for setting work perpendicular to a surface.

Parts. 1. Stock ⎫ Carbon steel, hardened and tempered all over and ground to a high
2. Blade ⎬ degree of accuracy.

The blade fits firmly in a slot machined in the stock and is held by three rivets counter-sunk on both sides. A small slot across the stock in the corner allows for any burrs on the metal which is being tested, thus avoiding a false reading.

This tool requires great care in handling because its value lies in its accuracy, which can so easily be destroyed by dropping. Small try-squares in the popular sizes are made from mild steel owing to the much higher cost of carbon steel and require even greater care as the edges can be burred more easily.

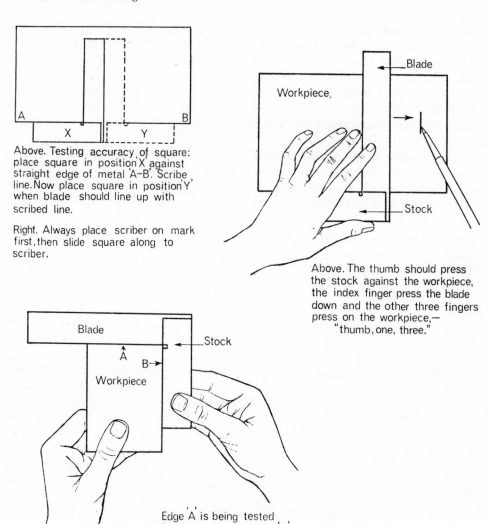

Above. Testing accuracy of square: place square in position X against straight edge of metal 'A-B'. Scribe line. Now place square in position 'Y' when blade should line up with scribed line.

Right. Always place scriber on mark first, then slide square along to scriber.

Above. The thumb should press the stock against the workpiece, the index finger press the blade down and the other three fingers press on the workpiece,— "thumb, one, three."

Edge 'A' is being tested for squareness to edge 'B'

Fig. 39   The engineer's square

OUTSIDE CALIPERS, Fig. 40

Use.   For measuring the diameter of round bars, and the width and thickness of metal.

Parts.   Two curved tapered legs with rounded toes and riveted or screwed together so that they can be opened and closed smoothly but rather stiffly.

When measuring a piece of metal the calipers are opened to the approximate size and

40

tried on the work. If the calipers then require opening a little, the joint end of the legs is lightly tapped on something solid, while if they require closing in, the outside of one leg is tapped instead. The calipers are to size when the toes lightly span the work. This is easy to understand, but it takes many years of practice to cultivate this light sense of touch. Spring calipers are adjusted by means of a knurled nut.

INSIDE CALIPERS, Fig. 41

These have straight legs tapering to form two toes which curve outwards and are jointed in the same way as the outside calipers. Inside calipers are used for measuring the diameters of holes, and

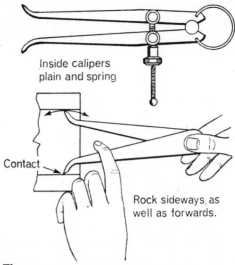

Inside calipers plain and spring

Contact

Rock sideways, as well as forwards.

Fig. 41

also the sizes of gaps and spaces in work pieces. The calipers are adjusted in the same way as the outside calipers and the setting is correct when the tool, gently rocked and swung with one toe held still, lightly touches the other side of the metal.

In many cases of fitting it is necessary to transfer a measurement from one caliper to another. This is done by setting one caliper to the given size and holding it in the left hand then adjusting the other caliper to just touch the toes of the first. The accuracy of work measured with calipers is only as good as the sense of touch or feel of the operator.

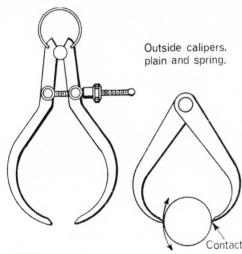

Outside calipers, plain and spring.

Contact

Fig. 40

HACKSAWS, Fig. 42

Use. For sawing small pieces of metal, e.g. sheet, bar and tube.

Parts. 1. Frame, one piece or adjustable⎫
      2. Handle, straight or pistol grip ⎬ various types
      3. Front bolt and pin, mild steel.
      4. Rear bolt and pin, mild steel.
      5. Wing or butterfly nut, mild steel.

The frame and handle is usually cast in one piece being of steel, aluminium or zinc based alloy and should be strong enough to remain rigid when the blade is strained between the pins. Adjustable frames are useful because they can be altered to take the two blade lengths, but for most work a 250 mm blade is adequate. The blade is mounted on the two pins with the teeth pointing away from the handle to give a forward cutting stroke.

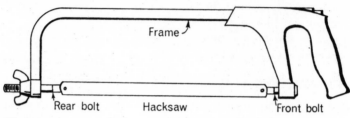

Fig. 42

Blades are to be had not only in different lengths but also in different teeth sizes as follows: 14, 18, 24 and 32 teeth per 25 mm.

Care must be taken when locating work in the vice for sawing to ensure at least three teeth are always engaged in cutting, otherwise the blade will jump and be difficult to move. For this reason tubing requires a fine-pitched blade (i.e. a blade having 32 teeth per 25 mm), as also does angle iron. Strip metal should be located so as to saw across the wide face and not down the narrow edge.

Blades are available hardened throughout or flexible having only the teeth hardened. The former are good in skilled hands but rather expensive and easily broken unless used correctly. When sawing, the right hand should grip the handle, with the left hand gripping the rear end of the frame. The left foot should point forward with the right foot behind, giving a comfortable balance to the body. Sawing should begin by lightly brushing the blade back across the work using the left thumb as a guide. As soon as a small clean cut is made the saw can be correctly held in both hands and the hacksawing gradually developed.

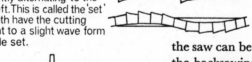

Large teeth are bent or set over slightly alternating to the right & left. This is called the 'set'. Small teeth have the cutting edge bent to a slight wave form to provide set.

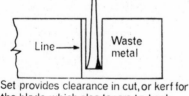

Set provides clearance in cut, or kerf for the blade which also tapers to back to assist this.

The blade should be quite tight and should cover as much of the work as possible to give even wear to all the teeth. The applied force should be only a little more than that required to hold and control the frame. Forcing the saw in the metal results in the cut curving off the line, an overheated blade, chipped and dulled teeth, and most probably a broken blade.

Fig. 43

The teeth of saw blades are bent alternately to the left and right throughout the blade length, Fig. 43. This is known as 'set' and enables the teeth to cut. The saw cut is therefore slightly wider than the blade thickness and is designed to give clearance to prevent the blade from jamming. As blades get worn, the dulled teeth lose their set and the saw cut is less wide than before. Hence, should a blade break when sawing, it is necessary to start cutting with the new blade at some different part of the work because the new blade will not enter the old saw cut.

There are occasions when a deep saw cut is required down a piece of metal and the hacksaw is the only tool available. This operation can be carried out by loosening the wing nut and removing the blade. The bolts are then free to be withdrawn slightly, rotated 90° and pushed back in their square holes. The blade is mounted on the pins as before, but is now at right angles to its normal position. Although the depth of cut by this method is unlimited, the width of metal is governed by the distance from the blade to the frame and seldom exceeds 100 mm.

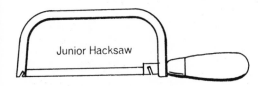

Fig. 44

However well one saws, the surface of the cut edge is rugged and must be filed, drawfiled and deburred to produce a good clean edge. Sawing must therefore be about 1 mm away from the scribed lines. Just as in filing we have to contend with the pull of gravity and file horizontally, so in hacksawing we always arrange our work to hacksaw vertically.

A very interesting and useful tool on the market is the Abrafile, which may be described as a round file for use with a hacksaw frame. It is ideal for clean-

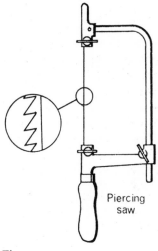

Piercing
saw

Fig. 45

ing out slots and following curved lines. Three different 'cuts' are available and a colour code aids identification. The 225 mm size will fit a 250 mm hacksaw frame. It is often known as a tension file.

For small, light work such as the sawing of rivets, screws, wire and thin sections, the Junior Hacksaw is a useful little tool enabling the operator to judge his weight better on fine work, Fig. 44.

For cutting intricate shapes in thin metal the piercing saw is used, Fig. 45. The frame is adjustable and allows broken blades to be used up. These blades, which are very thin, are held at each end by a clamp, the frame being squeezed in while fixing to obtain good tension. The teeth should point towards the handle because the cutting stroke is vertically

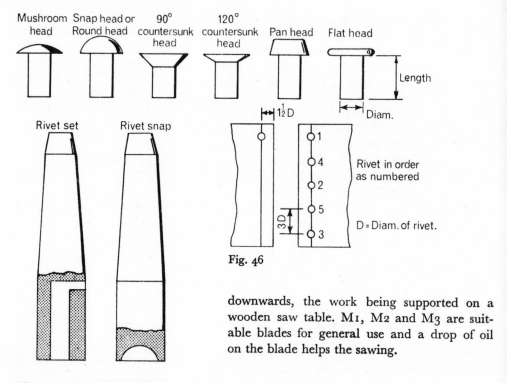

Fig. 46

downwards, the work being supported on a wooden saw table. M1, M2 and M3 are suitable blades for general use and a drop of oil on the blade helps the sawing.

Rivets and riveting

Rivets are used for the permanent joining together of metal. Four details must be known when selecting a rivet: 1. the length; 2. the diameter; 3. the shape of the head; and 4. the material of which it is made, Fig. 46.

Because it is impossible to drill a series of holes in two separate pieces of metal and expect them all to register exactly, the rule is to drill all the holes in the top piece of metal but only one hole in the bottom piece. After deburring all holes the plates are joined by means of one rivet. Work then proceeds by drilling the bottom plate through from the holes in the top plate one at a time and riveting up each hole as work proceeds, 'drill and rivet, drill and rivet . . . etc.'. To prevent buckling of the plates the holes are drilled in a special order, Fig. 46.

RIVET SET, Fig. 46

Use. For setting or closing together metal plates and ensuring that the rivet is right into the hole.

The tool is usually of carbon steel, hardened and tempered at the setting end, or it may be of any other softer metal such as brass when working on metals like copper and aluminium where marks are undesirable. The set consists of a suitable length of metal having a clearance hole for the rivet drilled in one end for about 25 mm along its length. It is placed over the projecting rivet tail and struck several times with a hammer so as to press the metal plates onto the rivet head.

RIVET SNAP, Fig. 46

Use. For shaping the tail of a rivet when riveting. If the tail of a rivet is to be shaped similar to a snap head it is said to be 'snapped over'. To do this a tool having a suitably shaped hollow in its end must be used to form the required shape and this tool is known as a RIVET SNAP.

After setting, the length of the rivet tail projecting should measure $1\frac{1}{2}$ times the diameter of the rivet. The tail is hammered down using a flat-faced hammer to give a sturdy bulge, then the snap is placed over and hammered to form a snap shape to the tail. During this hammering the head of the rivet must be supported and in the case of a countersunk head rivet it can be rested on any stout flat block of steel such as a chipping block. A snap head rivet however must be supported on something shaped to fit exactly over the head so as to preserve its shape. This support is called a DOLLY or BOLSTER, and it is usual to use another rivet snap for the purpose, Fig. 47.

For convenience of handling, it is common to combine the rivet set and the rivet snap in one tool to give a rivet set and snap, though they are available separately. If a countersunk is required, the countersunk in the metal should be made so that its diameter on the surface is twice the hole diameter, Fig. 48. After inserting the rivet and setting, the tail should project three-quarters of the rivet diameter above the surface. Fig. 49 shows how to produce a countersunk effect when riveting thin metal to thick.

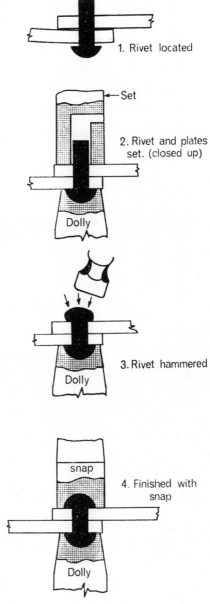

1. Rivet located

2. Rivet and plates set. (closed up) ← Set — Dolly

3. Rivet hammered — Dolly

4. Finished with snap — snap — Dolly

Fig. 47 Snap riveting

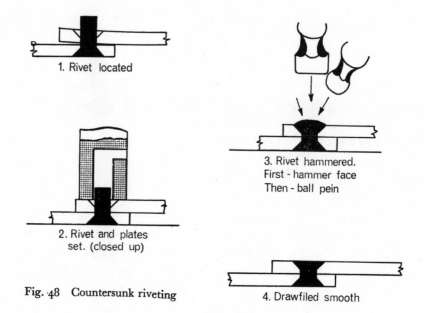

1. Rivet located

2. Rivet and plates
set. (closed up)

3. Rivet hammered.
First - hammer face
Then - ball pein

4. Drawfiled smooth

Fig. 48   Countersunk riveting

Where a countersunk rivet must be used on thin
sheet, countersink the bottom thick piece. Riveting
will pull the sheet into the countersunk hole.
This is called 'Dimpling.'

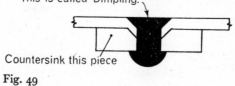

Countersink this piece

Fig. 49

46

6

Screw Threads, Stocks and Dies, Lubrication

SCREW THREADS

The wedge plays an important part in engineering, Fig. 50. Machine parts, such as wheels and shafts, are held together by keys which are flat wedges having a very long taper, and morse tapers are simply wedges in cone form. The drift used to separate the drill from its sleeve is a wedge used for the opposite purpose of uniting parts. The cutting action of most tools is made possible because they are wedge formed to enable penetration of the material and separation of the waste from the work. By means of slots and wedges it would be possible to assemble any piece of machinery though the end-product would appear very ungainly and cumbersome.

If we wrap a wedge form round a cylinder we produce a helix or screw thread and from this we have our nuts and bolts which are neater, more convenient and a better form of the wedge for certain purposes.

During the early days of engineering firms worked in isolation, with the result that all kinds of threads were being developed. As a result, Sir Joseph Whitworth, in 1841, designed and introduced a standard screw thread for all ordinary nuts and bolts.

Years later it was discovered that the pulsation and vibration from marine engines caused Whitworth-type nuts to slacken back. (In other words the wedge was too steep, and for better gripping the wedge had to be made with a finer or slower taper.) As a result, a finer thread system was evolved known as the British Standard Fine Thread.

In November 1965 the British Standards Institute strongly advised British industry to adopt the International Standards Organization (ISO) Metric Thread. The Whitworth, Fine and B.A. threads thus became obsolescent though it will be many years before they entirely disappear because of their use in existing equipment. This step was necessary for economy, efficiency and to assist our export trade with the many countries using the metric system.

The metric thread is V shaped and has a V angle of 60 degrees. The sizes range from 1 mm to 300 mm diameter. There is a coarse pitch series which is recommended for general work. There are also a variety of fine pitches. A coarse thread bolt is designated by the letter M followed by the sizes in millimetres, e.g. M6 × 30, which means a metric bolt, diameter 6 mm and length 30 mm. If a metric fine thread is required the pitch in millimetres must be stated after the diameter.

* Also see page 56.

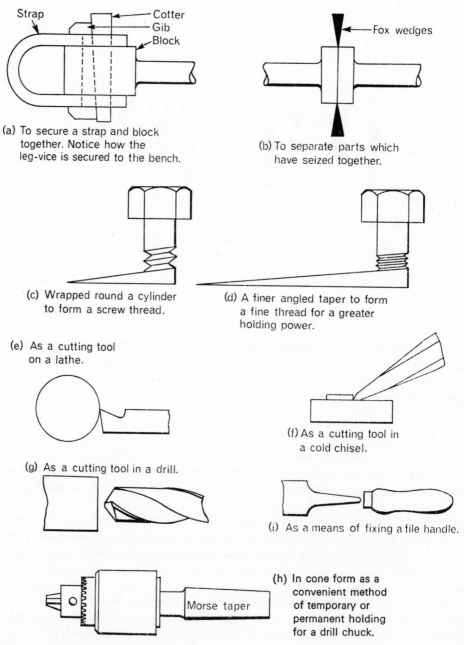

(a) To secure a strap and block together. Notice how the leg-vice is secured to the bench.

(b) To separate parts which have seized together.

(c) Wrapped round a cylinder to form a screw thread.

(d) A finer angled taper to form a fine thread for a greater holding power.

(e) As a cutting tool on a lathe.

(f) As a cutting tool in a cold chisel.

(g) As a cutting tool in a drill.

(i) As a means of fixing a file handle.

(h) In cone form as a convenient method of temporary or permanent holding for a drill chuck.

Fig. 50 Some applications of the wedge

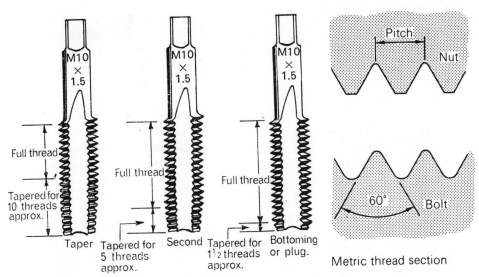

Fig. 51   Set of taps

TAPS AND WRENCH, Figs. 51, 52

Use.   For cutting a screw thread in a hole as when making a nut.

Parts. Taps—

   1. Taper
   2. Second   } these three taps comprise a set.
   3. Plug or bottoming

Wrench, for rotating the taps.

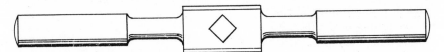

Fig. 52   Tap wrench

Taps are made from carbon steel, hardened and tempered all over, or H.S.S. Usually three or four flutes are ground along their length to form the cutting edges and also to facilitate waste metal removal. The metric size and pitch are clearly stamped on the shank and should always be checked before use. The end of the shank is square-shaped to take the wrench. The taper tap is tapered for about half its length so that the cutting of the thread is spread over many of the cutters on the tap, the second tap is tapered for about one-quarter of its length, while the plug or bottomer has only the first one or two of its threads tapered, the three taps being used in the order described.

49

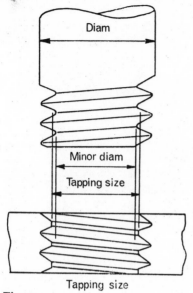

Fig. 53

Wrenches are obtainable in a wide range of designs, from the simple type having a plain square hole in the middle for the tap to the more elaborate adjustable types designed to fit several different sized taps.

When a thread is cut in a hole the operation is called tapping, but first the hole must be drilled in the metal. Theoretically, this hole should be the same size as the diameter of the bottom of the thread on the bolt and is known as the TAPPING SIZE, and the drill required to drill this hole is called the tapping size drill, Fig. 53. In practice the hole is made a little bigger than this to avoid straining the tap and to allow for the nature and flow of the metal and reference should be made to suitable charts showing the different tapping sizes which vary with different metals.

Having drilled the hole, both sides of it should be well deburred to remove the rough edges, prevent a ridge building up when tapping begins, and also give a measure of protection to the start and finish of the thread. The taper tap must be placed upright in the hole and the wrench fitted. The wrench is now rotated, pressing downwards to start the cutting of the thread. At the same time, the tap must be inspected from the front and side to check that it is square to the face of the work otherwise a drunken thread will result, that is, the nut will wobble when assembled on the bolt. With important work it is advisable to make use of the engineers' square. This is the most important part of the operation as once the tap has begun biting it cannot be corrected if needed.

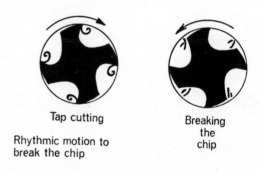

Tap cutting

Rhythmic motion to break the chip

Breaking the chip

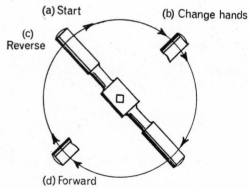

Fig. 54 Tapping action

50

After two or three turns the tap must be turned back a quarter turn to break off the waste metal chips, and from then on a rhythmic movement is used consisting of half a turn forward and a quarter turn back and forth, Fig. 54. Tallow or a sulphur-based oil should be used on steel, while paraffin or turpentine is best on copper and aluminium. Brass and cast iron should be tapped dry, the graphite in cast iron acting as a lubricant; also the metal chips crumble off so that the heat is quickly dissipated.

When tapping a blind hole, remove the tap regularly and shake out the waste chippings, Fig. 55. When tapping deep holes tap a few threads with the taper tap, followed by the second and the plug. The hole is then tapped deeper with the taper and again followed by the second and the plug. This procedure is continued using each of the three taps in turn until the thread has been made to the required depth. For shallow holes, it is enough to use each tap once, finishing off using the bottoming or plug to ensure an accurate thread. Taps should never be forced owing to the very great risk of breakage. It is generally agreed among experts that no tool is so easily and unexpectedly broken, and the removal of a broken tap fixed firmly in a hole may be a costly business.

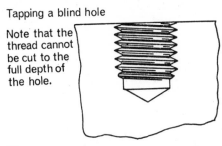

Tapping a blind hole

Note that the thread cannot be cut to the full depth of the hole.

Fig. 55

Stocks and dies

Use. For cutting a screw thread on a rod.

Parts. Dies, carbon steel, hardened and tempered all over, or H.S.S. They may be split circular or angular pattern.

Stocks and dies are available in many different forms, but the principle is exactly the same in all; that is, an adjustable hardened die, inside which the thread is cut, is securely held in a handle known as a STOCK, and rhythmically rotated in exactly the same way as the tap, thereby cutting a thread on the rod.

STOCK AND CIRCULAR SPLIT DIE, Fig. 56

The die consists of a cylindrical piece of H.S.S. or carbon steel, hardened and tempered all over. The thread is cut in a hole through the centre and has a slight chamfer at one end to facilitate starting the cut. Cutting edges and flutes are formed by the drilling of three holes which cut across the central threaded hole. Adjustment is made by a slit through the die, V shaped at the outer edge. The stock is flanged at the opposite side to enable the die to be correctly located and also to enable positive pressure to be applied to the die when in use.

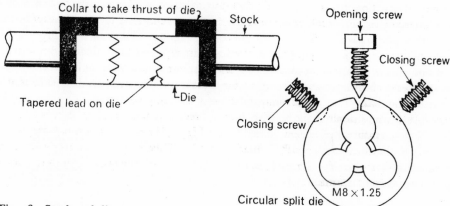

Fig. 56 Stock and die

The range of adjustment is small and is only intended to produce a tight or loose fit for the nut. Excessive adjustment may break the die or produce a badly cut thread. For a light cut the die is opened by screwing the central screw into the V groove. The grub screws on either side are now screwed up tightly to secure the die setting.

The rod to be threaded must have a taper filed on the end as an aid to starting the die, Fig. 57. Allowance for this taper must be made on the rod because it should be cut off afterwards to make a neat job. The taper should be about 5°-7° and equal in length to about one and a half times the diameter.

Just as for tapping, the stock and die must be pressed down on the rod and rotated clockwise, pausing to inspect the 'square-ness' of the stock and die to the rod from the front and side. Once the cutting is estab-lished, the stock must be turned back a quarter turn to break off the chippings. Rhythmic cutting, half a turn forward, quar-ter turn back and forth, proceeds until the thread has been cut as far down the rod as required. The tool is then wound back up the rod, removed and adjusted to take a further cut if necessary. Adjustment is

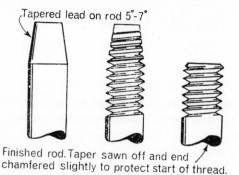

Finished rod. Taper sawn off and end chamfered slightly to protect start of thread.

Fig. 57

made by first slackening back the two side grub screws and then carefully slackening back the central screw, about one-third to one-half a turn. The grub screws are now tightened up again to hold the die in its new position.

Screwing is repeated and adjustment to the die carried out until the thread is cut to size, that is, when the nut fits smoothly on the rod. It is a good plan when nearing the correct thread size to run the die freely up and down the rod two or three times. This smooths out any irregularities and ensures a clean bright thread.

In actual practice the circular split dies do not always behave as described and one often comes across dies which when opened to their maximum cut a thread upon which the nut is a 'rattling' good fit!

For good-class work, split dies are often preferred because of their wider range of adjustment, there being many different types on the market. These split dies are in two separate pieces obtainable in pairs and with a code number on each to ensure that the correct dies are paired off. The simplest type is the angular pattern stock, sometimes called a Whitworth Stock, having V guides in a rectangular frame to position the dies and a bolt to keep them together when screwing, Fig. 58. Because of this bolt the handles are off set to the corners, hence the name, 'Angular'. The half dies are stamped '1' and '2' respectively, and should be mounted in the stock to match the corresponding numbers stamped on the stock frame.

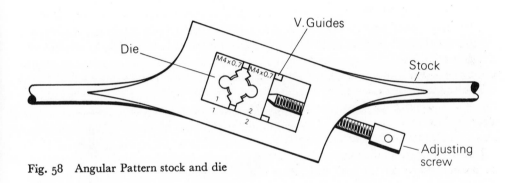

Fig. 58   Angular Pattern stock and die

The depth of cut is always increased by a slight turn, say a quarter to one-third, of the bolt which closes the two halves of the die together, and this is done with the stock wound up to the beginning of the rod.

Some stocks are available with a guide collar below the dies to help in keeping the tool square with the work. While probably useful on long plain rods, they interfere with screwcutting on short lengths such as bolts, because the guide prevents the die being run down into a shoulder.

It will have been observed that taps cut a thread to a fixed size and that no adjustment is possible. Dies, however, can be adjusted to cut a little metal off at a time thereby making the thread on the bolt to the desired fit. For this reason the nut must always be made first and the bolt cut to fit it.

When the threaded part of a rod must be held in the vice, a square nut of the same size should be sawn in half and used as vice jaws.

If a hole has to be drilled in a piece of metal so that the body of a bolt can pass through, it is necessary to drill the hole a little bigger than the diameter of the bolt body. The hole so drilled is known as a CLEARANCE HOLE, and the drill used is a CLEARANCE DRILL.

Cutting oils

REQUIREMENTS OF A MODERN CUTTING OIL

Good surface finishes can only be achieved by the correct use of a suitable cutting oil, and the fluid should have the following properties:

1. It must lubricate and cool the tool, chip and workpiece.
2. It must not cause corrosion.
3. The mixture must remain stable.
4. It must not be harmful.

There are two distinct types of cutting oils:

(a) Soluble oils, known as 'slurry', 'suds', or 'emulsion'.
(b) Neat oil.

SOLUBLE OILS are blends of suitable mineral oils with emulsifying agents so as to form a stable mixture with water, and are valued chiefly for their cooling properties. The dilution varies according to the operation but a useful mixture is one cupful of soluble oil to one gallon of water. When mixing, always add the oil to the water, stirring constantly.

In use, volume and not speed is the main factor, and the liquid should get right into the cutting zone.

NEAT OILS. These are used where lubrication must be maintained between the tool and the chip and prevents the waste metal building up on the tool edge when cutting hard alloys. Sometimes an extreme pressure (E.P.) quality is imparted to the oil by the addition of a sulphurized compound.

For normal workshop use soluble oil gives excellent results on all machining operations.

Soluble and neat oils—comparative properties.

DESCRIPTION	COOLING PROPERTIES	WETTING PROPERTIES	LUBRICATING PROPERTIES	TYPICAL OPERATIONS
Soluble oils (a) opaque (b) translucent	Excellent	Good	Fair	High speeds and roughing cuts on free cutting metals. Carbide-tipped tools.
Straight mineral oils	Fair	Fair	Good	Medium speeds and medium finishing cuts on free cutting and non-ferrous metals. H.S.S. tools.
Mineral oils with extreme pressure additives	Fair	Good	Excellent	Low speeds and heavy cuts on tough ferrous metals. H.S.S. tools.

General recommendations for soluble and neat cutting oils. This table is a rough guide only.

OPERATION	ALUMINIUM	BRASS	HARD BRASS	COPPER	MILD STEEL	MED. STEEL	TOUGH ALLOY STEELS
Tapping and Threading	Neat oil	Neat oil	Neat oil	Neat oil	E.P. neat oil	E.P. neat oil	E.P. neat oil
Drilling	Soluble oil	Soluble oil	Neat oil	Soluble oil	Soluble oil	Soluble oil	E.P. neat oil
Turning	Soluble oil	Soluble oil	Neat oil	Soluble oil	Soluble oil	E.P. neat oil	E.P. neat oil

Although cast iron is machined dry, a soluble oil is advisable on certain operations to lay the irritating 'dust'.
Unless there are difficulties such as overheating, brass is always machined dry.

Lubrication

Oil and grease are the life blood of engineering. No matter how smooth metal surfaces appear, they consist of hills and valleys so that when placed in contact they resist sliding. This friction, as we call it, can only be overcome by separating the two surfaces with a film of oil or grease.

Grease is ideal in dusty workshops because it seals the bearing against grit. It is also invaluable for slow-moving parts, bearings difficult to reach and places where oil would drip away.

Mineral oil of varying grades is used on high-speed bearings in particular, the design of which causes the lubricant to be drawn between the shaft and bearing by a wedge opening. Should this film be broken, the two metals will make contact, great heat will develop and the parts seize together.

7

Drills and the Grindstone

TWIST DRILLS

Use.   For cutting a round hole in a piece of metal.

Material. H.S.S. or carbon steel, hardened and tempered.

H.S.S. drills can be run at three times the speed of carbon drills but are more easily broken.

Flat drill

Positive rake for steel

Negative rake for brass

Fig. 59

The earliest form of drill was quickly and easily forged from a piece of plain carbon steel, filed to size and shape then hardened and tempered at the point. It was known as a flat drill, and sometimes a 'spade' or 'lip' drill, Fig. 59. It was simple to make, inexpensive and could be made to any desired size.

With the development of new engineering processes, however, the flat drill was found to be inefficient. The drilling of deep holes became a problem, partly because of the difficulty of the removal of waste metal, partly because the drill tended to wander out of line as drilling progressed, and also because the action was one of scraping rather than one of cutting. Further, the cutting edges dulled owing to overheating through chip blockage in the hole, and it soon became clear that some

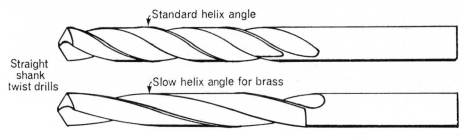

Standard helix angle

Straight shank twist drills

Slow helix angle for brass

Fig. 60

C

form of corkscrew shape was necessary to enable the waste metal to escape. As a result of many experiments in this direction an American called Morse developed the twist drill we now know and which is named after him, Fig. 60. This is the most widely used type of drill today, being accurately ground to size.

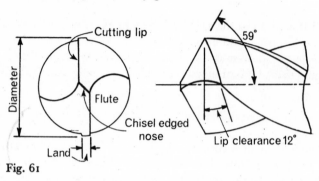

Fig. 61

Generally, two helical flutes with a helix angle of 25° serve to remove waste metal, but for special work drills having more flutes and with varying helix angles are used. To reduce friction between the body of the drill and the work, the body is 'relieved' or reduced slightly in diameter but leaving a thin band of metal at the leading edge of the flutes. These thin bands are known as the LANDS, and are ground cylindrically true to form the drill diameter, Fig. 61.

The two cutting edges or lips are formed by the flutes meeting the end of the drill and are ground to make an angle of 59° with the main axis of the drill. Clearance is obtained by grinding the ends of the drill away behind the cutting edges at about 12° to prevent the drill end rubbing on the metal instead of cutting, Fig. 61. It is important that the two cutting edges are ground at the same angle and are equal in length, otherwise a large hole will result, the size being governed by the length of the longer cutting edge.

Gauges should always be used to test the cutting angles to see that they are equal, also that the cutting edges are the same length and with the chisel nose in the centre.

Parallel shank twist drills are gripped in a three jaw self-centring chuck, the chuck key being used in all three holes to ensure even strain and gripping power. Morse taper shank drills are held in the drill spindle socket by wedge action.

The tapered parts must be clean and dry, when they can be assembled by pushing smartly together

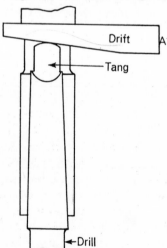

Fig. 62

with the tang end of the drill in line with the slot in the sleeve. The drills are easily removed by tapping a steel wedge, known as a DRIFT, in the slot. A piece of wood just below the drill will protect the nose when it falls out of the sleeve, Fig. 62.

DRILL SPEEDS

The speed of a drill is taken as the speed at the outside edge and is the distance a drill would travel in one minute if laid on its side and rolled. A moment's thought will show that for smaller drills the speed must be increased proportionally to the diameters for the same material being drilled. Hard metals require slow speeds while soft metals and brass require fast speeds.

FEED

The feed is the distance the drill cuts into the metal in one revolution and is fast for soft metals but slow for hard metals. Too slow a feed causes the drill to rub and quickly dulls the cutting edges, while too high a feed wears down the drill corners, causes overheating and may even burn the drill.

DRILLING

The chisel edge of the drill nose must always be guided into the work by means of a small dent in the metal, using a hammer and a centre punch for this purpose. For ordinary work where accuracy is not so important, it is enough to pop mark the metal using the hammer and centre punch, and ensure that the conical dent is big enough to take the nose of the drill, Fig. 63. The work is then suitably held and drilled.

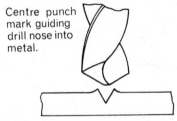

Centre punch mark guiding drill nose into metal.

Fig. 63

For accurate work, the hole centre must be marked out by two fine scribed lines intersecting at right angles, the intersection being the hole centre. This point is first lightly pop-marked then the hole size is marked out using dividers and lightly pop-marked eight times for clarity. The central pop-mark is now enlarged for the drill nose, the work is securely clamped for drilling and a little of the waste metal removed from the work with the drill. The work is then inspected to ensure that the slightly dished hole now made is concentric with the marked-out circle. If it is, drilling proceeds, giving the hole another check just before the body of the drill enters the work. If, however, the slightly drilled depression is not concentric with the marked circle, it has to be 'drawn over'. This is done by using a round-nosed chisel and chipping a groove right down the depression, beginning at the side to which the drill must be drawn and grooving to the bottom. This provides a new centre and the groove enables the drill to move over to the new position. If necessary, this may be repeated several times, but once the body of the

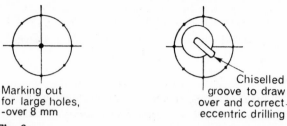

Marking out
for large holes,
-over 8 mm

Chiselled
groove to draw
over and correct-
eccentric drilling

Fig. 64

drill enters the metal the hole position cannot be altered, Fig. 64.

When drilling large holes say 18 mm diameter and over, difficulty is experienced in feeding the drill into the work due to the length of the chisel nose, which merely scrapes. The difficulty is overcome by drilling a smaller hole first, called a pilot hole, the drill diameter being just a little more than the length of the chisel edge of the large drill.

The most dangerous and difficult part of drilling is when the drill passes through the metal at the other end of the hole. If the force is not reduced the drill will burst through the metal with a jerk forming two thick burrs, one to each flute which either hold the drill and break it, or cause the drill to snatch the work from its clamps and spin it round with alarming, if not dangerous results.

As the drill approaches the other side of the metal, the operator will feel when the feed is becoming easier and must then apply less pressure to the drill so that it passes slowly and smoothly out of the other end of the hole.

An ordinary twist drill can be used for drilling through tinplate provided that the two cutting edges are ground nearly square across, because the nose must not penetrate the other side of the metal before the cylindrical body of the drill has entered the hole.

A twist drill tends to dig in and seize when drilling brass but this is avoided by using a slow helical fluted drill.

MORSE TAPERS

The Morse taper is simply a cone-shaped wedge which permits quick and easy assembly and separation of drills and chucks from machines. The wedge is tapered approximately 52 mm per m and is made in eight sizes to suit differ-. ent sized drills, No. 0 being the smallest and No. 7 the largest. Sockets and sleeves are also obtainable so that different sized drills may be built up to fit any machine, Fig. 65. The mating parts must be clean and dry when they can be assembled easily by a quick push home, making sure when a drill is being used that its tang is correctly housed in the sleeve slot. The drive is through the tapered sleeve of the drill and not the tang. For most work, the Morse tapers in common use are Nos. 1, 2 and 3.

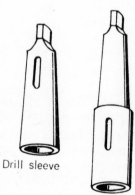

Drill sleeve

Drill socket

Fig. 65

The DRIFT used to remove the drill from its sleeve has a taper of 145 mm per m or an angle of 8°—19'.

DRILLING MACHINES

Types. 1. Sensitive, taking drills up to 6 mm diameter.
   2. Bench or pillar, taking drills up to 12.7 mm and sometimes 19 mm diameter.
   3. Heavy duty pillar and radial machines, taking all sizes of drills and covering a wide range of work.

Only 1 and 2 will be considered here.

Use. For drilling, countersinking, counterboring and spotfacing.

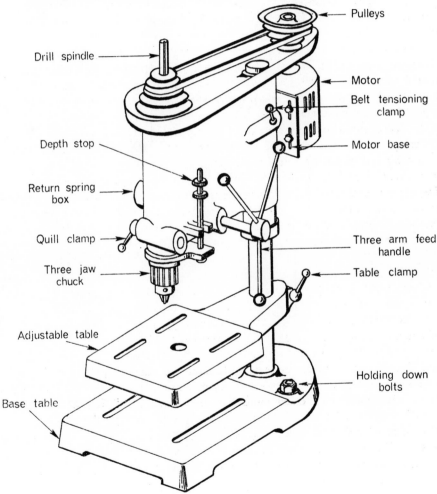

Fig. 66   Drilling machine with belt guard removed

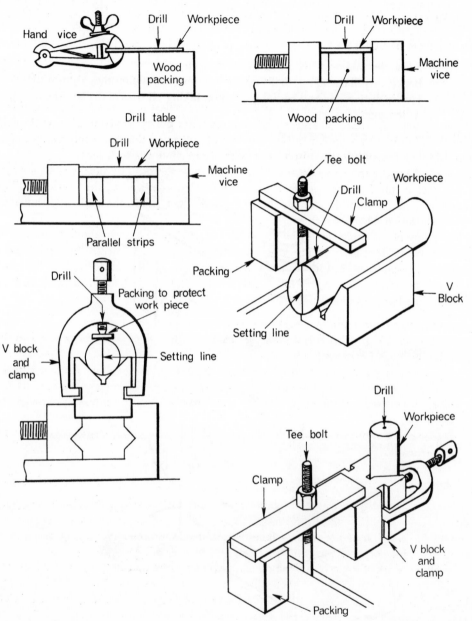

Fig. 67   Holding work

The sensitive drilling machine is a small light machine taking drills up to a maximum of 6 mm diameter. High speeds and a light feed are essential for small holes, which thus enables the operator to feel the work being performed by small drills, hence the name sensitive. Bench or pillar drilling machines are obtainable in a large number of shapes and sizes for all classes of work, and quite a number of them would prove equally satisfactory for most purposes, Fig. 66.

Different metals and different size drills demand a variety of speeds from the machine. This is arranged by means of several different diameter pulleys keyed to slide on the drill spindle and driven by a similar but inverted set of pulleys on the motor spindle. For most work, four or five speeds are ample, and quite often three are sufficient.

A spoked handle transmits downward movement to the quill by means of a rack and pinion and a spiral return spring in unwinding raises the quill to the top again. The spindle is mounted in ball races which are fixed at either end in the quill, and shoulders ensure a positive downward drive to the drill.

The fixing of the table should be such that the drill point is only about 15 mm or so above the work, thus giving a minimum distance of travel to the drill. Cooling oil and a small brush should be handy if required.

It must be emphasized again that all work must be securely held for drilling and the following methods suggest the more usual ways of holding work, Fig. 67.

1. HAND VICE for holding small work such as thin sheet and strip.
2. MACHINE VICE. This is a popular method, but the vice should be secured to the table by bolts for extra safety.
3. CLAMPS AND BLOCKS. Clamps are made of steel and may be any shape to suit the job. Blocks are used to support one end of the clamp while the other rests on the work so that when the holding down nut is tightened up the clamp can press on the work and hold it.
4. V BLOCKS AND CLAMPS for holding cylindrical shaped work either horizontally or vertically.
5. ANGLE PLATE.
6. Any combination of the foregoing.

Slots are provided in the drilling machine table for the use of holding-down bolts which should be of as large a diameter as possible. Packing must always be used to support the work so as not to drill holes in the machine table. Wood suffices for most small work, but for accuracy parallel strips should be used.

For bench work, a HAND DRILL taking drills up to 7.9 mm diameter is popular and useful Fig. 68. A high speed with a very light feed is essential to avoid the drill 'digging in'. Having drilled the hole, the drill should be kept rotating in the same direction when being withdrawn so as to clean the hole and clear out the waste.

The BREAST DRILL, Fig. 68, is a larger version of the hand drill and takes drills up to 12.7 mm diameter. A curved plate is fitted at one end for the operator's body to press against when in use. Two speeds are usually available, the driving handle being easily

63

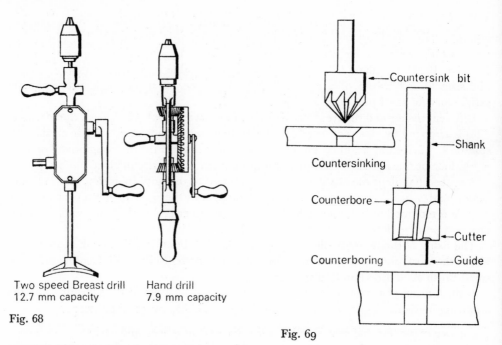

Two speed Breast drill
12.7 mm capacity

Hand drill
7.9 mm capacity

Fig. 68

Countersink bit

Shank

Countersinking

Counterbore

Counterboring

Cutter

Guide

Fig. 69

changed from one spindle to the other. Because of the extra weight of this tool it is useful for jobs in awkward places.

SOME FURTHER OPERATIONS ALLIED WITH DRILLING

COUNTERSINKING, Fig. 69. This is performed by a countersink bit having a nose angle of 90° or 120° and consists of opening out the end of a hole to a cone shape so as to take a countersunk head rivet or screw. When assembled, the head lies flush with the surface of the metal.

COUNTERBORING, Fig. 69. This operation consists of opening out the end of a drilled hole so as to take, for instance, the cylindrical head of a cheese-headed screw and allow the head to lie flush with the surface of the metal.

The tool used to perform this operation is known as a counterbore and looks like a short drill having several flutes.

WASTE METAL, Fig. 70, shows various methods of removing waste metal by drilling.

The grindstone

THE GRINDSTONE is a wheel of abrasive particles 'glued' together which revolves at high speed so that it cuts metal, especially for tool sharpening. Corundum and emery are natural abrasives, but with harder steels artificial abrasives such as aluminium oxide and carbide of silicon are necessary.

GRIT AND GRADE. The 'grit' is a number which denotes the grain size and refers to the number of meshes per 25 mm length through which the abrasive will just pass. The grade refers to the strength with which the grit is bonded together. The correct grade is one which permits the worn grains to be pulled loose from the grindstone thus exposing new cutting points of fresh grains to the workpiece, and varies according to the metal being ground. In general, soft metals require a hard grade and hard metals a soft grade.

The tool rest must be secured as close to the wheel as possible, goggles should be worn and the work applied lightly to the front of the stone. Never grind on the side as this will probably burst the wheel.

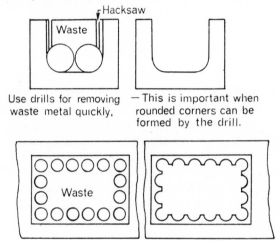

Use drills for removing waste metal quickly,

— This is important when rounded corners can be formed by the drill.

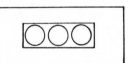

When drilling more than two holes, use a slightly smaller drill to reduce possibility of cutting into workpiece.

To remove large area of waste metal by chain drilling

(a) Mark out lines 3 mm inside hole size. Step off 5 mm intervals. Pop mark. Drill holes 4 mm.

(b) Chisel through from both sides. File to line.

For thin metal, drill a 4 mm hole in one corner and use abrafile or piercing saw.

Fig. 70   Methods of removing waste metal

c*

8

The Forge

The craft of the blacksmith began in the very beginning when men found iron in the ashes of their fire and hammered it to shape. In medieval times he became most important because his skill supplied the wants of the mason, carpenter, farmer, armourer and locksmith.

The forge, Fig. 71

Use. For heating metal so that it can be altered in shape by hammering.

The blacksmith's forge may be built of bricks, or castings, or angle iron and mild steel sheet, or may even be a combination of any or all of these materials, but generally for small use it consists of a shallow steel box on angle-iron legs. The steel box, known as the hearth, holds the fire and should have about 75 mm of sand or firebrick in the bottom to avoid burning through the metal base. The remainder of the hearth is filled up with small coke which in time forms a compact mass. Above the hearth is a hood to collect smoke and fumes from the fire which are then led outside by a suitably sized flue pipe and chimney.

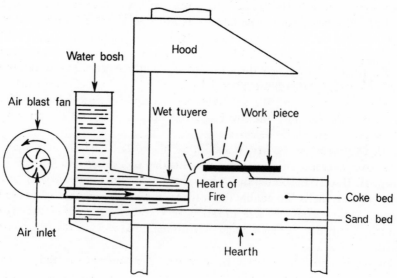

Fig. 71   The Forge

To maintain and control the fire temperature, air is supplied under pressure by hand or motorized fan through a cast iron pipe called a tuyere, or more commonly a tue. Because of the heat of the fire, the tue soon burns away if it is a solid pipe or casting known as a DRY TUYERE. It is much more economical in the long run to pay extra for a WET TUE, which lasts a lifetime, than to replace dry tues at intervals. Wet tues are castings having a water jacket all round the air blast hole. The casting is bolted to a water tank (or water bosh as it is more often called) at the rear of the forge and this tank must always be full of clean water.

The best fuel to use is small walnut-size coke breeze or Bawco Beans, though small coal is popular with some smiths.

THE FIRE

If a wet tue is fitted, first check the water bosh to see that it is almost full of clean cold water. Remove coke and clinker from in front of the air blast hole so as to make a depression about 200 mm in diameter. Turn on the air blast gently to start air blowing through and apply a flame from a gas poker. The position of the poker should be adjusted until the air catches the flame and causes it to roar. Fresh coke is now added round it without smothering the flame. There should be at least one sharp dagger of flame shooting out of the fire which will ensure heating the cold air in the chimney and get the draught going up.

The air blast should now be increased to speed up the lighting of the fire. Having removed the gas poker the air supply should be reduced to a minimum, for, although we must have air to supply oxygen to the fire to keep it burning, excess oxygen will attack the heated metal placed in the fire and cause scale to form. It has been said that one can always tell a bad blacksmith by the large amount of scale around his anvil.

After the fire has been burning for some time it may appear to turn dull and burn on one side. This is caused by a lump of clinker or slag forming and gradually blocking up the air flow. The remedy is to reduce the air speed, open up the fire carefully and remove the red-hot clinker, using the rake and slice. The hot fuel is then quickly returned to the tue mouth, fresh fuel added and the air blast stepped up to bring the fire to its normal working condition. Not until the fire has burnt up properly and the air supply been reduced should forgework be resumed.

When placing metal in the fire, it should be placed horizontally and under the top layer of hot coke to ensure moderate and even heating plus protection from the oxygen in the air, Fig. 71. If work is pointed down into the heart of the fire it will only be a matter of minutes before it melts. To enable the work to be placed horizontally means building up the fire so that it is about the size and shape of a football with half of it above the level of the hearth. The fire must be attended to continually, as entry and withdrawal of work disturbs it.

After forging has been in progress for some time the water in the bosh at the back of the forge will be seen to get quite hot and even boil. This is not serious, especially if the forge has been in constant use for some time, for as long as there is water in the tank the

67

tue will not burn. However, it is worth while checking to see where the fire is as beginners tend to push it to the back of the hearth and over the tue casting. The chemical action which we call fire takes place where the air blast meets the fuel so around this spot must develop the fire.

Air may be supplied by large double-acting bellows, and though pleasantly quiet in use, must be worked frequently to keep the fire going. The most convenient form of air blast supply is probably that obtained from a small fan driven by an electric motor. Air is sucked in axially through a wire-mesh filter and flung centrifugally to the rim, where it is sent speeding along the tue. For most work, sufficient air blast is supplied when the motor is run on the first or second notch of the rheostat, and only occasionally has the motor speed to be run beyond this.

Blacksmiths' tools

TONGS Various shaped jaws, Fig. 72

Use.   For holding and picking up hot metal.

Parts.   1. Handles or reins.
          2. Pin.
          3. Jaws.

Material. Wrought iron or mild steel.

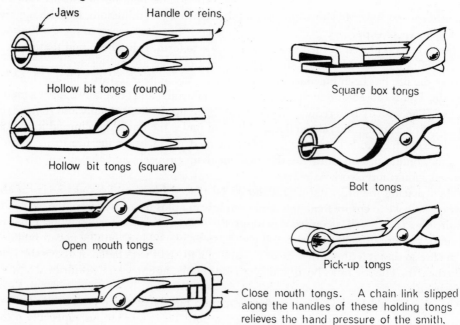

Jaws   Handle or reins

Hollow bit tongs (round)

Square box tongs

Hollow bit tongs (square)

Bolt tongs

Open mouth tongs

Pick-up tongs

Close mouth tongs. A chain link slipped along the handles of these holding tongs relieves the hand pressure of the smith.

Fig. 72 Tongs

68

Tongs are made in lengths from 400 to 650 mm in steps increasing by 50 mm, and are sold by weight. They are many and varied to suit a host of operations but only the more common types will be dealt with here.

OPEN MOUTH TONGS

When the handles of these tongs are closed the flat jaws are parallel and open, being suitable for the gripping of thick sheet.

CLOSE MOUTH TONGS

With these tongs, when the handles are closed, the flat jaws are parallel and almost touching, being thus suitable for the gripping of thin sheet. The jaws of all tongs must grip the work for the whole of their length to avoid slipping. If the jaws do not fit properly they must be heated in the fire and hammered to fit the work along their length.

HOLLOW BIT TONGS

When the handles are closed, the jaws meet and have a hole along the middle of their length. In some cases the hole is round, and in others it is square, formed by a V groove in each jaw. These tongs are used extensively for picking up and holding cylindrical or 'round' stock and square bar, and are made in several sizes denoting the size of material they will hold.

SQUARE BOX TONGS

Similar to open mouth tongs but having a lug on either side of the upper jaw. This is a useful tool for gripping strip work which has to be often turned on two adjacent sides.

BOLT TONGS

Similar to the hollow bit tongs but having shaped jaws to accommodate a bolt head while the body is being gripped.

PICK-UP TONGS

Useful for picking up hot work and holding it while securing a grip with other tongs.

ANVIL, Fig. 73

The anvil is the blacksmith's bench or work table and must be sturdy and strong to withstand the heavy pounding it receives from hammers of all sizes. It is available in weights from 25 kg to 200 kg, but for schools an anvil weighing from 50 to 75 kg is ample. Anvils used in the past to be made from wrought iron with strips of carbon steel welded together across the face, but nowadays they are normally made from mild steel with or without the carbon steel face. The anvil, which consists of a rectangular face upon which most of the work is done, should be mounted on a cast iron or wooden stand

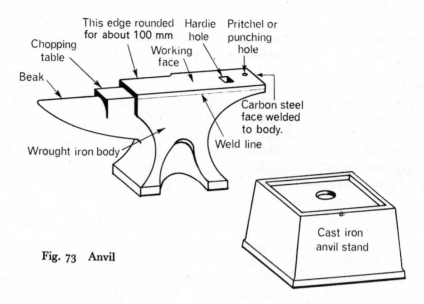

Chopping table

This edge rounded for about 100 mm

Hardie hole

Pritchel or punching hole

Working face

Beak

Carbon steel face welded to body.

Wrought iron body

Weld line

Fig. 73   Anvil

Cast iron anvil stand

so that this face is just above knee height and slopes slightly away from the operator with the anvil beak pointing to the left.

Between the face and the beak is the table upon which chopping out can be done so as not to damage the face. The beak is useful for curved and circular work and no doubt owes its shape to the demand for horse shoes in olden days. The hardie hole is used for holding the shank of the hardie as well as the bottom tools of swages and fullers which are used in pairs. The punching hole serves to take a length of rod when the end is being worked into shape such as the head of a bolt. The far edge of the anvil face at the L.H. end has about 100 mm of its length rounded over to enable smooth bends to be made in metal. The anvil is thus a composite tool which has slowly developed over the centuries to its present shape.

HARDIE, Fig. 74

A tapered square-shanked cast steel chisel designed to fit in the hardie hole of the anvil and used by the smith for cutting up small stock. The metal is placed across the cutting edge of the hardie and struck with a hammer, causing a cut. The metal is reversed and hammered on the hardie again and repeated until there are four deep cuts in it at right angles to each other. The fracture is completed by holding the metal across the face of the anvil with the cuts on the edge and tapping the metal beyond, when it will snap off.

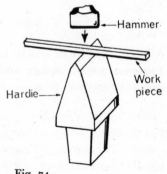

Hammer

Work piece

Hardie

Fig. 74

FULLER, Fig. 75

Usually worked in pairs and consisting of a top and bottom tool. The bottom fuller is shaped to fit in the hardie hole, while the top fuller is equipped with a metal or hazel stick handle, the latter being more shock absorbing. They are made in a variety of sizes denoted by the diameter of the rounded edge, and 8 or 10 mm is a useful size for general work. Fullers are used for 'necking', i.e. forming a rounded groove in metal, and also for making a rounded corner or fillet where two faces meet at an angle, sharp corners always being avoided in forgework in case of cracks developing.

SWAGE, Fig. 76

This tool consists of a top and bottom grooved part forming the complete unit, the lower fitting in the hardie hole and the top being fitted with a metal or hazel wood handle. Swages are obtainable in different sizes, the size denoting the diameter of the cylinder it will shape.

Top and bottom fuller

Fig. 75

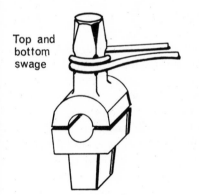

Top and bottom swage

Fig. 76

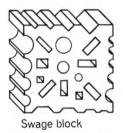

Swage block

Fig. 77

Flatter

Fig. 78

SWAGE BLOCK, Fig. 77

A heavy steel block containing a varied assortment of grooves around the edges, also numerous round, square and rectangular holes through the body. The swage block should be securely mounted in a stand similar to the anvil cast-iron stand.

FLATTER, Fig. 78

For flattening and smoothing off straight faces and areas of work. The face is flat with rounded edges to avoid marking the work. A useful size is 50 mm square. Again, the handle may be metal or hazel.

SET HAMMER, Fig. 79

This tool is used for flattening in awkward corners where the flatter cannot get. It is fitted with a wooden handle exactly like a sledge hammer and with a face smaller than the flatter, being only about 30 mm square.

Set hammer

Fig. 79

HOT CHISEL, SETT OR SATE, Fig. 80

A slender chisel fitted with a handle and made from carbon steel for strength. It is so called because it is used for cutting hot metal and cannot therefore be hardened and tempered. The cutting edge is ground to about 40°.

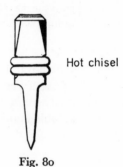

Hot chisel

Fig. 80

COLD CHISEL, SETT OR SATE, Fig. 81

This is a stoutly made chisel fitted with a handle and made from carbon steel. The edge is ground to the normal chisel angle of 60° and is hardened and tempered. It is so called because it is used for the cutting of cold metal. With both the hot and cold chisel the cutting edge should be slightly convex along the length to avoid the corners being broken off.

When cutting along a line the chisel should tilt slightly so that the cut is deeper at the back and so guides the chisel. This method ensures one clean cut along the metal.

Cold chisel

PUNCH, Fig. 82

May be round or square and is used to push a hole in red-hot metal. A punched hole preserves the grain flow of the forging.

DRIFT, Fig. 82

A cigar-shaped tool used for truing up and correcting a punched hole.

HAMMERS, Fig. 83

A variety of these is necessary for applying force to the many tools used by the smith as well as being the direct means of shaping hot metal. The smith's assistant, or striker, uses a sledge hammer weighing from

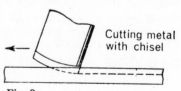

Cutting metal with chisel

Fig. 81

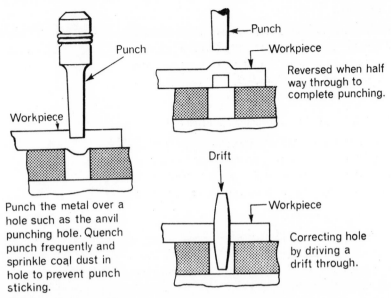

Punch

Workpiece

Punch the metal over a hole such as the anvil punching hole. Quench punch frequently and sprinkle coal dust in hole to prevent punch sticking.

Punch

Workpiece

Reversed when half way through to complete punching.

Drift

Workpiece

Correcting hole by driving a drift through.

Fig. 82 Hole punching

1.8 to 3 kg, though in industry hammers up to 6 kg are available for heavy work. Beyond this range steam hammers are employed.

For the smith's own use, hammers from 450 g to 900 g are in general demand.

MEASURING

When dealing with hot metal a brass rule is most suitable because it is unaffected by heat. Other tools can be made from brass as the need arises, a square for instance being very useful. Inside and outside calipers are handy as they enable actual contact to be made with the hot metal. Ordinary mild steel is suitable for the making of these.

GENERAL

A rake, slice and a poker are essential for the cleaning and maintaining of a good fire, removing clinker and patting the hearth flat.

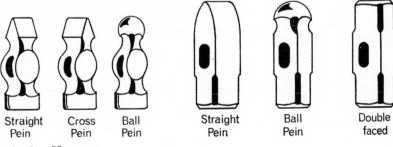

Straight Pein   Cross Pein   Ball Pein   Straight Pein   Ball Pein   Double faced

Fig. 83 Hammers

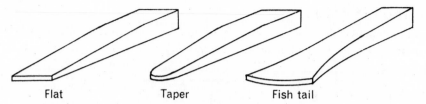

Flat Taper Fish tail

Three ways of shaping ends to be scrolled

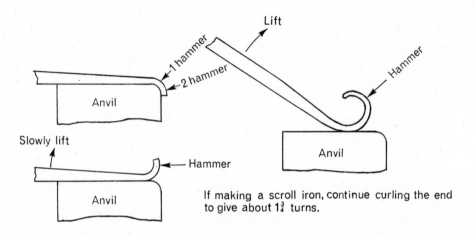

Lift

1 hammer
2 hammer

Hammer

Anvil

Anvil

Slowly lift

Hammer

Anvil

If making a scroll iron, continue curling the end to give about 1$\frac{3}{4}$ turns.

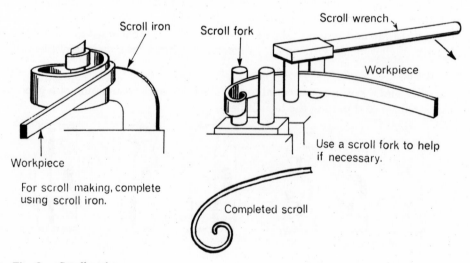

Scroll iron

Scroll fork

Scroll wrench

Workpiece

Workpiece

For scroll making, complete using scroll iron.

Use a scroll fork to help if necessary.

Completed scroll

Fig. 84 Scrollwork

74

SCROLL IRON, Fig. 84

Made from rectangular strip steel, say, 25 × 8 mm for normal work. The end is fish-tailed and offset to make a one sided taper, then scrolled to act as a former for the making of scrolls.

SCROLL WRENCH, Fig. 84

These act as extra hands and are used to help the metal round the scroll iron and adjust the curve.

SCROLL FORK, Fig. 84

Similar to the scroll wrench but held in the vice. Strip metal can be curved and scrolled by feeding it through the fork and bending it a little at a time. It can also be used for adjusting scroll shapes.

9
Some Forge Operations

UPSETTING, Fig. 85

This is considered to be one of the most difficult operations in forgework. It involves heating a piece of metal to red heat and then hammering or banging it on the anvil face to swell the heated part. It is usually performed (a) on the end of a rod for the forming of a bolt head, and (b) in a length of metal so that it can be bent to an angle without distortion taking place at the bend due to compression and tension in the metal.

Successful upsetting depends upon confining the bright heat to a very limited length of the metal, otherwise the heated metal will bend. Local heating is achieved by getting the metal hot and then quenching out quickly the unwanted heat, using either a water bosh or a small can depending upon where the heat is.

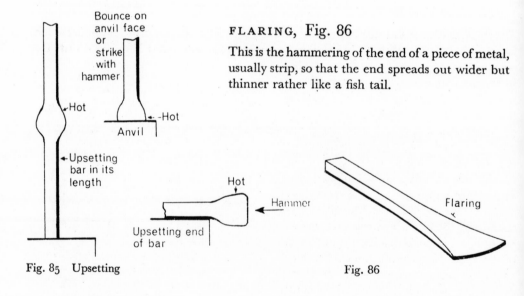

FLARING, Fig. 86

This is the hammering of the end of a piece of metal, usually strip, so that the end spreads out wider but thinner rather like a fish tail.

Fig. 85   Upsetting

Fig. 86

FULLERING, Fig. 87

Apart from 'cogging' or drawing down, fullering is employed for necking or grooving metal prior to shaping. Necking has the effect of preserving the grain flow in the metal.

Forging a piece of metal develops a fibrous grain flow which strengthens it.

Fullering compresses grain flow.

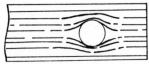

Punched hole.
A little grain flow has been severed because a piece of waste metal has been removed but some grain flow has been developed round the hole.

Fig. 87

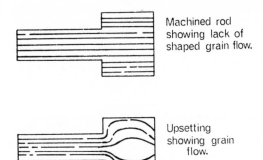

Machined rod showing lack of shaped grain flow.

Upsetting showing grain flow.

TWISTING, Fig. 88

The stock, square or flat strip, should be marked off, using a centre punch to indicate the length of metal to be twisted. The work is then uniformly heated for some distance beyond the pop marks to allow for chilling by contact with the vice and tongs. The hot metal is quickly located in the vice with the lower pop mark just visible, and the tongs or wrench placed to grip just above the other pop mark. It is then twisted by rotating the tongs as many times as required, usually one to one and a half complete turns being sufficient.

Care must be taken to keep the work straight as there is a tendency to wander out of line and develop a kink at both ends of the twist. Not working quickly enough causes an uneven twist, due to the metal cooling out unevenly, it being hotter in the middle and cooler where gripped. For small work, below 10 mm square for example, it is better to anneal the metal and twist it cold, thereby producing an even twist.

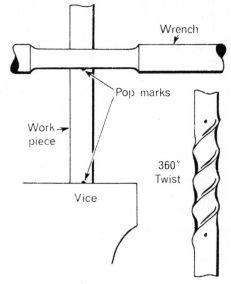

Fig. 88   Twisting

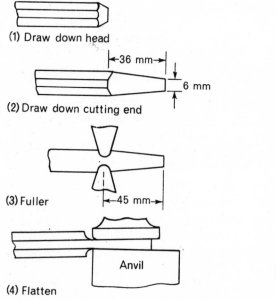

(1) Draw down head

(2) Draw down cutting end

←36 mm→

6 mm

(3) Fuller

←45 mm→

(4) Flatten

Anvil

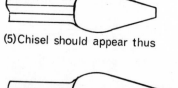

(5) Chisel should appear thus

(6) Draw down point to 3 mm to trim up

(7) Grind 60° angle cutting edge.
Point harden and temper purple.

Fig. 89 Forging a cross cut chisel

FLATTENING, Fig. 89

The hot work is placed on the anvil face and hammered, making it thinner and causing it to spread in all directions. Large areas of hammered work can be smoothed off by using a flatter and the assistance of a striker. The flatter should be used whenever possible to finish off a piece of work, but for awkward corners the set hammer should be used.

DRAWING DOWN, Fig. 90

This operation reduces the section of a piece of metal, making it longer. The principle is that if a strip of metal is squeezed between two parallel cylinders, the metal is made thinner and longer, but the width remains the same. In practice, the cylinders are the beak of the anvil and the straight pein hammer, though the ordinary hammer will do for small work.

Where the reduction is great and extends over a long length of bar, drawing down is performed much quicker and easier by using the top and bottom fullers and an assistant (a 'striker') with a sledge hammer. The operation is then known as 'cogging' and the bar assumes a wavy appearance as the fullers dent their way along the bar. The hot metal is then turned through 90° and the whole operation repeated along the new surface until the required smaller section is reached. The work is finally finished off smooth by means of the flatter and sledge hammer.

Drawing down on a small scale is carried out quite simply by using the ordinary hand

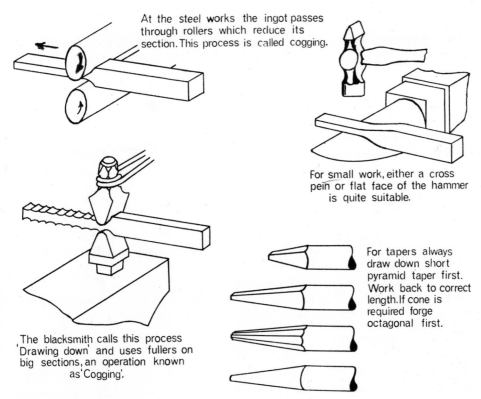

At the steel works the ingot passes through rollers which reduce its section. This process is called cogging.

For small work, either a cross pein or flat face of the hammer is quite suitable.

The blacksmith calls this process 'Drawing down' and uses fullers on big sections, an operation known as 'Cogging'.

For tapers always draw down short pyramid taper first. Work back to correct length. If cone is required forge octagonal first.

Fig. 90   Drawing down

hammer and striking the hot metal on the beak of the anvil and slowly passing it back and forth, Fig. 90. Tapering is a form of drawing down and this is performed by first drawing down a short point, and then gradually working back to increase the length of taper until the correct size is reached, Fig. 90.

If a piece of metal is hammered continuously all round its circumference the outer part expands, and breaks away from the inner part, resulting in the end of the metal splitting. To avoid this disaster all metal should be hammered on two adjacent sides only, no matter what its section either at the beginning or in the finished product. If the metal is square and has to finish square, then this is no problem.

With round stock the method is to draw down just as if the metal were square, then when the correct size is reached the corners are hammered to produce an octagonal section, finally finishing off using a swage, swage block or creasing iron to give the finished round shape. The thumb should be laid along the top of the tongs or metal as a guide to indicate the face being hammered first. By turning the wrist outwards the metal is rotated 90° and the thumb is now at the outside indicating that the second edge is being forged.

PUNCHING, Fig. 82

A punched hole is better than a drilled hole because the grain flow of the metal is preserved. A hardened steel drift is finally hammered through to correct the size and shape.

Development

When a strip of metal is bent to an angle, the material on the inside of the bend is compressed while that on the outside is stretched. If the metal is thin, this is not noticeable and bending is easily performed. When the piece of metal is thick, however, the compression on the inside is great enough to cause the metal to buckle sideways while that on the outside is narrowed and distorted and may even crack.

If we think of a strip of metal as being built up of many thin layers, we can understand more easily how each succeeding outside layer has to stretch more to follow the bend while each succeeding inside layer is subject to a greater compression. It follows from this that there must be a thin layer somewhere in the metal which is neither compressed nor stretched, and this layer is in fact the middle one.

To calculate the correct length of metal required to form a bracket, therefore, it is only necessary to calculate the length of this 'middle layer' or neutral axis as it is more properly called.

Suppose it is required to know the length of metal needed to forge a loop or eye on the end of a piece of steel, the inside diameter of the loop to be 30 mm and the thickness of the metal 6 mm, Fig. 91. Because the neutral axis is the middle line of the metal all the way round, the diameter of the neutral axis is 36 mm. The length of the metal required to make the loop will be the length of the neutral axis which is equal to the circumference of the 36 mm diameter circle.

$$= \pi \, . \, D$$
$$= 3.14 \times 36 \text{ mm}$$
$$= 113 \text{ mm of metal required}$$

The blacksmith is not worried about such details as π and uses a formula of his own which gives excellent results considering the nature of his work. His formula is:

$$3 \times \text{inside diam. of loop} + 4 \times \text{thickness of metal used.}$$

In this particular case he would get:

$$3 \times 30 + 4 \times 6 \text{ mm of metal}$$
$$= 114 \text{ mm of metal required}$$

which in forge work is as close an accuracy as would be required.

To calculate the length of steel required to make the bracket shown, Fig. 92, in all cases it is essential to know the thickness of the metal, the radius of the bend and the

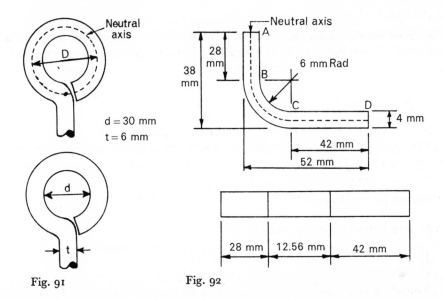

Fig. 91   Fig. 92

angle of the bend. To find the length of metal required, divide the drawing up into straight lengths and curves, and calculate the length of each part in turn, working along the neutral axis at all times. In this case we have from A to B, a straight length of 28 mm, from B to C a quarter of a circle, and from C to D a straight length of 42 mm. The metal required for the right-angled curve is found by finding the circumference of the circle of which the neutral axis from B to C forms part, then dividing by four because from B to C is one quarter of a circle.

Radius of N axis is $6 + 2 = 8$ mm

∴ diam. of N axis is 16 mm

and circumference is 16×3.14 mm

and $\frac{1}{4}$ of this is $16 \times 3.14 \times \frac{1}{4}$ mm

$= 12.56$ mm

Therefore the exact length of metal required to make the bracket is $28 + 12.56 + 42$ mm, which is 82.65 mm.

It might be argued, of course, that the bracket could be bent from a longer strip of metal and then sawn to length afterwards. Although this is possible it is not workmanlike and would be quite wasteful of material, especially if many similar components were required.

If a ⊔ shaped bracket had to be made, then accurate calculation and workmanship would be the only way of producing the item. The ⊔ bracket is simply an extension of the ∟ bracket, but as the two parallel arms must be a specified distance apart, the length of the neutral axis must be properly calculated if accurate work is to result.

When the bend is not at right angles it should be remembered to work from the angle through which the strip has been bent from the flat when calculating the curved part. Thus, if a strip of metal is bent to make an acute angle of 45°, it has been bent through an angle of 180° − 45° = 135° which is ⅜ of a circle, so that ⅜ of the circumference will have to be found when calculating the curved length of the neutral axis.

Finding the lengths of the various parts when unfolded and laid out in the flat is known as DEVELOPING, and we speak of finding the DEVELOPMENT of an object. More difficult problems are seen to be simply extensions of the basic principles.

Examples in forgework

CROSSCUT OR CAPE CHISEL, Fig. 89

1. Hacksaw off stock 150 × 12 mm across the flats, octagonal carbon steel.
2. Draw down the head on two sides for 10 mm long using anvil beak.
3. Round off head chamfer—octagonal first then finally round.
4. Draw down blade end to square taper, 36 mm long by 6 mm square at end.
5. Pop mark 45 mm from end and neck in from both sides using top and bottom fullers. Reverse work frequently to keep necking even. Finish full 5 mm thick.
6. Flatten blade to obtain slight taper for clearance. Use flatter, sledge hammer and anvil face.
7. Draw down blade leaving it 18 mm broad at the rear and 56 mm long from the neck.
8. Finish off with flatter on anvil face. Do not attempt to produce a thin edge as this will only burn away during heating.
9. Remove the scale on the blade using an old file, then draw file bright. File or grind the edge to 60°. Point harden and temper purple.

FORGING AN EYE OR LOOP from 450 mm of 8 mm square mild steel, the internal diameter of the loop to be 30 mm, Fig. 93.

1. Calculate the length of metal required to form the loop from the smith's simple formula: 3D + 4t.

    That is: 3 × 30 + 4 × 8 mm

    = 90 + 32 mm

    = 122 mm
2. Make a pop mark on the metal 122 mm from one end.
3. Heat to a bright red heat and hammer along two corners of this 122 mm length on the face of the anvil to produce an octagonal section.

4. Finish off to 8 mm round section using top and bottom swage.

5. Bend to a right angle at the pop mark, using the pritchel hole or leg vice so as to produce a sharp bend.

6. Heat the metal and localise the heat to the 122 mm length by quenching water over the remainder of the metal. This will ensure a true loop and a straight rod.

7. Place the heated metal on the anvil beak or bick iron, and beginning at the end, tap it down and work back to form as much of the loop as possible.

8. Now place the metal under the beak and tap it down to close the eye. Remember to hit just beyond the point of contact between hot metal and anvil otherwise damage and distortion will result to the work.

9. Final adjustment can be made by tapping the loop on or just beyond the anvil face.

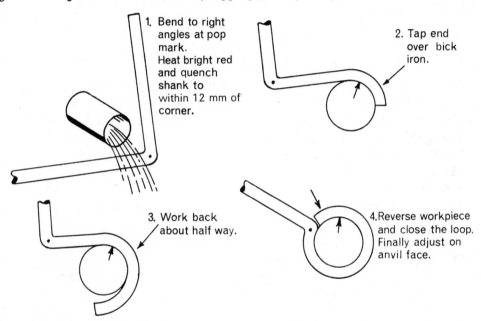

1. Bend to right angles at pop mark. Heat bright red and quench shank to within 12 mm of corner.

2. Tap end over bick iron.

3. Work back about half way.

4. Reverse workpiece and close the loop. Finally adjust on anvil face.

Fig. 93   Forging an eye or loop

SCROLLWORK, Fig. 84

The end of the workpiece should be shaped and curved so that it hooks on the end of the scroll iron. At red heat it is then wrapped round the iron, using a scroll wrench to assist the operation and pausing every 20 mm or so to lower the workpiece slightly to produce a flat scroll, though it can be trued up easily on the anvil face.

The exact shape should be marked out on a sheet of black steel and is usually done by tracing from the drawing. Adjustment is made by means of the scroll wrench and fork to get the workpiece to the final shape.

10

Tinsnips, Tinplate, Joints, Beaded and Wired Edges

TINSNIPS, Fig. 94

Use.   For cutting tinplate and non-ferrous metals up to about 1 mm thick.

Parts.   1. Handled blades, carbon steel, hardened and tempered.
   2. Rivet, for securing the blades together.

Tinsnip sizes are denoted by their overall length which varies from 150 mm to 350 mm. Straight tinsnips are used for cutting straight and convex curves of large radii, while the curved tinsnips are used for concave curves. Universal or Gilbow Shears are used for both straight and curved cuts, being particularly useful for intricate shapes. When resharpening, blades should be ground and sharpened on their edges only, and never on their inside faces.

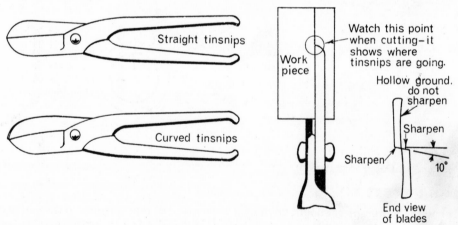

Fig. 94   Tinsnips

   The cutting action is one of shearing and the blades should be held at right angles to the surface of the metal being cut to avoid nipping it between the blades. Except when cutting in a corner, the ends of the snips should never be used otherwise the metal will be buckled.

84

FOLDING BARS, Fig. 95

Use. For enabling a length of sheet metal to be folded, usually to 90°.

Parts. Two parallel blades, mild steel.

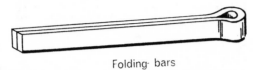

Fig. 95   Folding bars

The blades are made from one strip of rectangular steel bar forged to shape and having a loop at the bend to provide a spring action for the slight opening and closing of the blades. The work is inserted between the blades which when released spring tightly together and hold the metal quite firmly. For accurate work, better folding bars can be made by machining two stout rectangular strips of steel and locating them to each other by dowels for accurate alignment of the true faces.

THE GROOVER, Fig. 96

Use. For finishing the shape of wired edges and rounded joints in sheet metalwork.

Parts. Made in one piece from carbon steel, and consists of the shank for holding and the former which is semicircular in section and hardened and tempered.

The tool is obtainable in several sizes denoted by the width of the groove, which is the diameter of the semicircle.

SEAM SET, Fig. 97

Use. For setting down and locking folded seam joints.

Parts. Made in one piece from carbon steel and consists of a shank for holding and a former of rectangular section which is hardened and tempered.

The tool is obtainable in several sizes denoted by the width of the groove section.

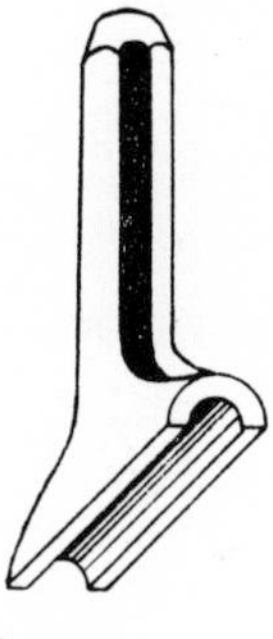

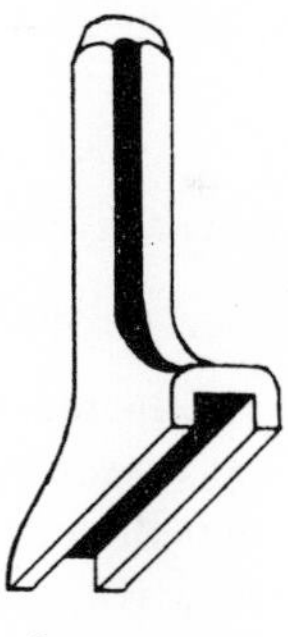

Groover   Seam set

Fig. 96   Fig. 97

BENCH SHEARS, Fig. 98

Use. For cutting thick sheet metal and bar generally up to about 6 mm thick.

Parts. 1. Frame, mild steel
2. Bottom blade
3. Top blade or Cropper } carbon steel hardened and tempered all over.
4. Steady, mild steel.
5. Handle, mild steel.

85

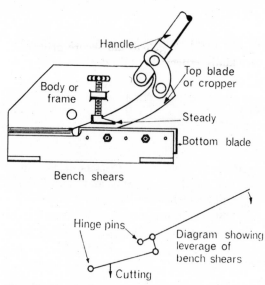

Bench shears

Fig. 98   Bench shears

Screws are usually fitted in the frame to enable the bottom blade to be adjusted close to the top blade to obtain clean cutting, and prevent the nipping of thin metal between the blades. The principle of operation of the bench shears is based upon the lever, that is, it is more convenient to apply a small force through a long distance than it is to apply a large force through a short distance to perform a set piece of work. Very often it is the only way to get the work done. Nothing is gained except convenience, which is referred to in engineering as mechanical advantage.

The bench shears consists of a lever operating a lever so as to increase the mechanical advantage and enable thick metal to be sheared with ease.

Maximum mechanical advantage is therefore obtained by opening the jaws and putting the metal as far in as possible and holding the handle as near the end as practicable.

PLIERS, Fig. 99

Use.   For gripping and manipulating thin sheet, tube, rod and wire.

Material. Carbon steel, with hardened and tempered jaws.

COMBINATION PLIERS

One of the most useful and popular of the pliers having toothed jaws for gripping flat and round stock and two blades for cutting wire and small cable. Blades are also to be found on the edges for shearing small wire. These pliers are popular with electricians and the handles are often heavily insulated as a protection against electric shock.

GAS PLIERS

These have jaws shaped to grip two different diameters of pipe and are coarsely toothed for secure holding. A small groove in the nose end enables the tool to be used as a pin vice while one handle is tapered to form a lever for prising purposes.

ROUND-NOSED PLIERS

A light and useful tool with two cone-shaped jaws which are ideal for gripping circular work without marking it. Loops can also be formed in wire by twisting it round the jaws.

FLAT-NOSED PLIERS

A light and handy tool with thin tapered jaws lightly ridged to aid secure gripping. These pliers are useful for small work of many kinds, especially when dealing with wire and thin sheet.

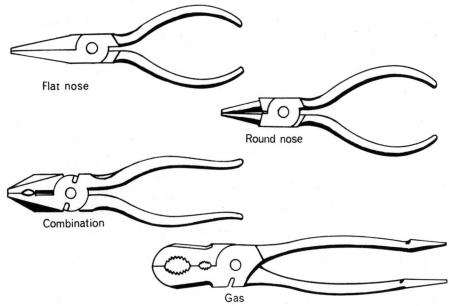

Flat nose

Round nose

Combination

Gas

Fig. 99   Pliers

STAKES, Fig. 100

Use.   To support and assist the correct shaping of metal.

Material. Carbon steel, often welded to mild steel stock for economy.

The carbon steel is hardened and tempered to resist wear. Stakes are made substantial in size and weight to provide ample support when in use. The surface used for working on should be smooth and bright, while the rest of the tool is usually painted as a protection against rusting. When not in use the polished face should be oiled. Sheet metal firms stock scores of stakes of every size and shape each for a particular job but only the main types will be considered here.

BICK IRON

This tool has the appearance of a very slender anvil. The long tapered beak enables rings to be formed and shaped in addition to short cylindrical work.

FUNNEL STAKE

For shaping and truing conical work but can also be used for rings.

Funnel

Bick iron

Hatchet

Half moon

Creasing iron

Raising stake

Round bottom   Cannister

Fig. 100   Stakes

HATCHET STAKE

Used for folding sheet metal to an acute angle of about 60°, and is used after the metal has been folded to right angles in the folding bars.

HALF-MOON STAKE

Just as the folding bars are used for folding over metal in a straight line, the half-moon stake is used for folding metal over on a circular line. This process is known as 'throwing up' and occurs when making the bottom disc to fit on a cylindrical can.

Tinman's anvil

CREASING IRON

A sturdy stake with a good anvil face for general work and a series of graded semicircular grooves across one half of the face for truing up beaded edges and aiding the making of wired edges. This stake is also useful when truing up rod.

TINMAN'S ANVIL

A handy anvil for use at the bench. The face is flat and smooth, three edges are straight and one is curved.

BOTTOM STAKE

For work on the bottoms of cylindrical articles. The face is flat and smooth and the side is machined to a slight taper for clearance between the stake and the work.

CANNISTER STAKE

This is similar to the bottom stake but the side is machined parallel to form a cylinder.

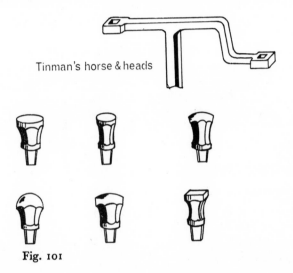

Tinman's horse & heads

Fig. 101

RAISING STAKE

A cylindrical arm with a slightly rounded edge to avoid cutting the workpiece. Used for raising shapes from flat sheet to bowl and vase forms by hammering.

A useful tool is the tinman's horse and six heads, Fig. 101. The horse enables the heads to be held well clear of the bench and vice so that large work can be manœuvred about with ease.

A solid foundation is essential for all stakes due to the hammering and pounding they receive, and a section of a tree trunk is ideal for this.

CHIPPING OR CHISELLING BLOCKS

These are solid blocks of mild steel designed to stand on the bench and give sturdy support for all manner of hammering operations. A useful size is 300 mm square by 50 mm thick.

D

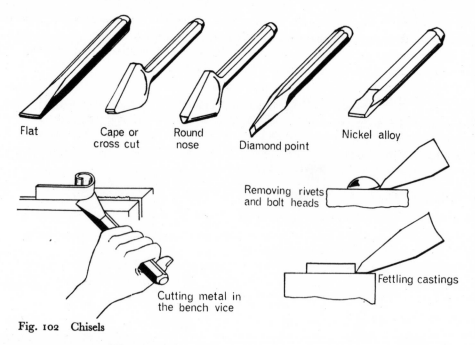

Flat   Cape or cross cut   Round nose   Diamond point   Nickel alloy

Removing rivets and bolt heads

Fettling castings

Cutting metal in the bench vice

Fig. 102   Chisels

COLD CHISELS, Fig. 102

Use.   For cutting cold metal.

Parts. Made from one piece of octagonal carbon steel and includes:
1. The head, for striking.
2. The shank, for holding.
3. The blade, for cutting.

The chisel is point hardened and tempered and ground to form a cutting angle of 60°. The head is chamfered to reduce the burring over in mushroom fashion from constant hammering. When the burr does form, however, it must be carefully removed by filing or grinding owing to the danger from flying splinters.

FLAT CHISEL

This is the most commonly used chisel of all, cutting flat sheet, small rivets, bolts and nuts and in general cutting metal in all sorts of difficult places. The blade is slightly wider than the shank to prevent the tool sticking in the work. The actual cutting edge is ground to an angle of 60° and is slightly convex curved along its edge to prevent the corners from digging in and marking the work surface.

When cutting sheet metal in the vice, the work is fixed with the line just along the vice jaws. The chisel is held at an angle of about 45° to the length of the metal and raised 30° from the horizontal. Cutting is begun by placing the edge of the chisel against the metal with the chisel resting on the vice. Steady, even blows with the hammer will send the chisel along the top of the vice cutting the metal away as it goes.

Beginners make the mistake of looking at the head of the chisel while chipping, but should keep their eyes on the cutting edge as work proceeds.

CAPE OR CROSS-CUT CHISEL

A chisel having a much narrower blade than its shank, strength being provided by giving depth to the blade part. As before, the cutting edge is made slightly wider for clearance and the blade is ground to 60°. The crosscut chisel blade is ground quite straight and is useful for cleaning out grooves.

DIAMOND-POINTED CHISEL

So called from the shape of the nose. A useful tool for chipping in corners.

HALF-ROUND CHISEL

Similar in shape to the cross-cut except that the underside is semicircular in shape. A very useful tool for the cutting of rounded grooves such as oilways in bearings. It can also be used for correcting the start of a wrongly drilled hole.

ALLOY CHISELS

The plain carbon chisels just mentioned have a carbon content of about 0.75 per cent and their cutting edges require frequent regrinding and occasional hardening and tempering to keep them in good condition. A big improvement is obtained in the use of alloy steel for chisels which stand up to hard work for a very much longer period. The alloy consists of medium steel (about 0.4 per cent carbon) and approximately 3 per cent nickel with a trace of manganese. A file is used to clean up the cutting edge for use.

This peculiarity of a nickel chisel arises from the fact that the cutting edge work hardens in use, though it remains soft enough for sharpening by filing. Nickel-chromium is another popular alloy for cold chisels, and having similar properties. Some chipping operations are shown in Fig. 102.

Standard wire gauge

Sheet metal is obtainable in many thicknesses and before metrication each thickness was given a number, known as the GAUGE, for easy reference. Hardened gauge plates are available having slots round their edges to enable these thicknesses to be quickly checked, Fig. 103.

The Imperial Standard Wire Gauge (I.S.W.G.) and the Birmingham Gauge (B.G.) are the only two legally recognized gauges in Great Britain but these will gradually be replaced by gauges for metric sizes. Meanwhile, it is advisable to state the thickness of metal in millimetres.

I.S.W.G. plate

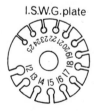

Fig. 103

SHEET-METAL WORK

Refers to the craft of making up articles from thin sheet metal, often tinplate.

Tinplate is made from mild steel having a low carbon content, not more than 0.1 per cent and sometimes known as dead mild steel. The steel is thoroughly scoured and cleaned all over and passed first through a bath of liquid flux and then through a bath of molten tin in one long continuous ribbon of steel. The tinned plate is next smeared with palm oil and passed between rollers which produce a smooth even surface. Finally, the metal is cut into convenient sheets for handling and packing.

Modern methods include electrolytic tinning which produces a more even coating of tin than by the dipping process. Tin is one of the most expensive metals in general use in engineering, so it is easy to understand why the coating is no more than 0.01 mm thick. Where a thicker coat is required, the plates are dipped again to give two coats, and these are known as DOUBLES. Tinplate is used mostly in the food-canning industry owing to the resistance of tin to food acids, and the ease with which the tinplate can be soft soldered.

Marking out on tinplate should be done by means of an H.B. pencil sharpened to a chisel edge. This will ensure that the tinplate is not damaged.

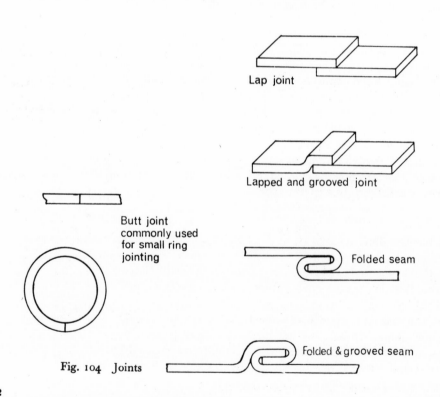

Lap joint

Lapped and grooved joint

Butt joint commonly used for small ring jointing

Folded seam

Folded & grooved seam

Fig. 104 Joints

Joints, Fig. 104

BUTT

This is the simplest method of joining two pieces of metal, but is only suitable for thick sheets where the edges present a large surface for the making of a strong joint.

LAP JOINT

This joint consists of simply fitting one edge of metal over the edge of another piece.

LAPPED AND GROOVED JOINT

This joint is exactly the same as the plain lap joint except one plate has been joggled to make the joint flush on one side, and also bring the two plates into the same plane.

FOLDED SEAM

A stronger joint, made by allowing the width of the joint on one piece of metal and twice the joint width on the other piece. The two edges are hooked over, joined and tapped down to make a tight joint, which should be soft soldered if it is required to be air or watertight.

FOLDED AND GROOVED SEAM

This is the same as the folded seam joint except that it is made to lie flush on one side by

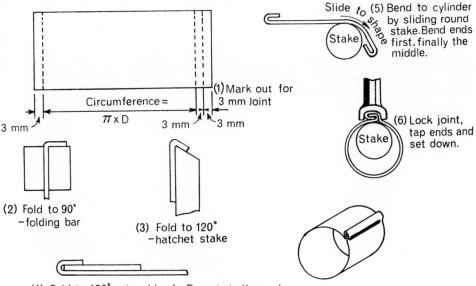

(1) Mark out for 3 mm Joint

Circumference = $\pi \times D$

3 mm   3 mm   3 mm

(2) Fold to 90° – folding bar

(3) Fold to 120° – hatchet stake

(4) Fold to 180° onto old rule. Repeat at other end.

Slide to shape (5) Bend to cylinder by sliding round stake. Bend ends first, finally the middle.

Stake

(6) Lock joint, tap ends and set down.

Stake

Fig. 105   Making a folded and grooved seam joint

means of a seam set. When setting out the folded seam joints, the allowances must be 'bare' owing to the thickness of metal when folding, Fig. 105.

These joints just mentioned may be used for joining sheet metal in the flat or when making up boxes and cylindrical cans.

EDGED OVER OR 'SNUFFED ON' BASE, Fig. 106

A common and simple method of fitting a circular base to a can. It is usual to allow 3 mm for the joint on metals like tinplate and this is gradually tapped over the edge of the half-moon stake until the edge is 'thrown up'.

It is important to tap the edge down a little at a time, rotating the disc first nearly horizontally and then lowering it a few degrees each complete revolution to enable the edge to shape up. The blows from the mallet should be light, quick and applied at the same point throughout the operation. Should the base buckle, it can be tapped flat using a hammer and a block of wood while resting the metal on a smooth flat surface.

For the final fitting, the edge should be tapped inwards to grip the sides of the can and so make a good tight fit before finally soldering in place.

Edges

The edges of metal are thin and weak besides being dangerous when handled, and must be treated in some way to overcome these drawbacks.

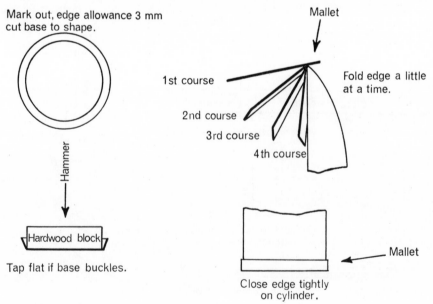

Fig. 106   Making an edged over base

BEADED, Fig. 107

This is the simplest method of treating an edge and provides strength, safety and good appearance. The edge is first tapped over to a right-angled bend using folding bars and a rawhide mallet. Next the edge is turned over further on a hatchet stake to give an acute bend. It is then placed on a bench and the edge tapped down further on to an old rule. Finally, the edge is knocked down carefully to touch the main body of the metal, care being taken not to hit the actual curved bead which provides the strength. Sometimes the beaded edge is finished off with soft solder.

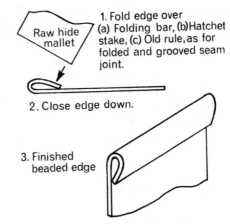

Fig. 107 Making a beaded edge

WIRED EDGE, Fig. 108

This is a more robust edge being simply a beaded edge reinforced with wire. The allowance of metal to make a wired edge is two and a half times the diameter of the wire used. Having marked off this allowance, the edge is tapped over using folding bars preferably

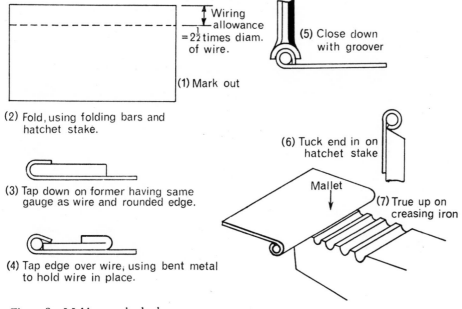

Fig. 108 Making a wired edge

having a rounded edge to preserve the curve. Next, tap the metal further round a radiused bar to produce a semicircular edge, an operation which can be performed with the metal flat on the bench.

The wire, straightened and rubbed with tallow to lubricate it during working, is now placed in the groove and held in place tightly by means of an old rule or thin strip of steel slightly thinner than the diameter of the wire. Tallow is better than grease as a lubricant because it does not interfere with the later operation of soldering. The metal is struck down over the wire a little at a time along its length, and finally closed in tightly by tapping the wired edge on the hatchet stake, or using a chisel made in the same form as a hatchet stake for hand use. The wired edge can be trued up by using a hand groover or the creasing iron. Where a lapped joint is to be made in a can and the wire is thin, the wired edge can be made in the flat and the can then shaped into a cylinder round the bick iron. To avoid a weakness where the two ends of the metal meet it is usual to arrange the wire so that the join is about 10 mm from the metal edge, thus producing a stronger joint. A small offcut of similar wire is temporarily used while the wired edge is being knocked up, and preserves the shape while forming the cylinder. The short length is then discarded and the protruding end of the wire is tucked in place to meet its other end, Fig. 109.

If a can is to be made with a folded joint, it is not possible to wire up in the flat as explained above because it is impossible to hook the joint together and also tuck in the wire.

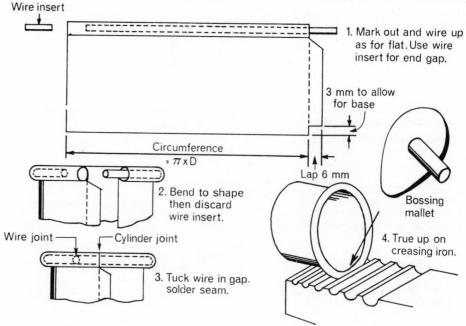

Wire insert

1. Mark out and wire up as for flat. Use wire insert for end gap.

3 mm to allow for base

Circumference = π x D

Lap 6 mm

2. Bend to shape then discard wire insert.

Wire joint — Cylinder joint

3. Tuck wire in gap. solder seam.

Bossing mallet

4. True up on creasing iron.

Fig. 109   Wiring cylinder edge

In this case, the wired edge is made after the metal has been marked out, bent and hooked up complete. The edge is flanged over, the wire inserted and the flange then worked down and tucked in.

Rectangular boxes and other straight-sided articles are wired up after the box has been made, the wire being bent to shape and placed in position with the joint in the middle of one long side.

When setting out, study the drawing to get the main overall sizes. Mark these out then add on the various allowances for jointing, edges and base.

I I

Soldering

The word 'solder' is of foreign origin and means to make solid. Soldering is the joining together of two metals by a lower melting point alloy resulting in a solid metallic joint.

Soldering may be soft or hard, the latter often including brazing which requires the highest temperature of all.

Soft soldering

Soft soldering is applied to small parts where strength is unimportant, as for instance the multitude of soldered wires and terminals in radio, television and other electrical work, instruments and tinplate articles of all kinds as well as metals having a low melting point such as lead. In all soldering, the melting point of the solder should be well below that of the metal being soldered, the melting point of soft solder ranging from 183°C. to about 250°C.

Soft solders are basically alloys of TIN and LEAD with sometimes a little ANTIMONY for strength and hardness. By varying the proportions of tin and lead several different

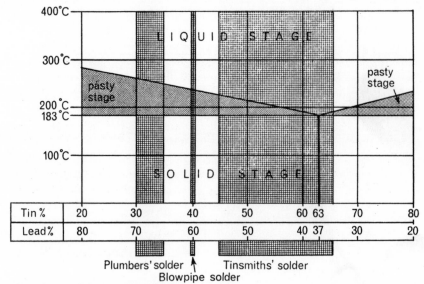

Fig. 110   Soft solder melting chart

solders can be made each having different characteristics making them suitable for a wide variety of soldering work. Most mixtures result in pastiness between the solid and the liquid stage, the extent depending upon the proportions of the metals, Fig. 110.

The beginner must guard against soldering with the copper bit when the solder is in the plastic state because this indicates an iron not hot enough. When using a soldering iron, the solder on it must be quite liquid.

Although there are many grades of soft solder, only the more common will be considered here, as follows:

Melting range

	TIN	LEAD	SOLID	LIQUID	PLASTIC RANGE
Plumbers' solder	30	70	183°C.	250°C.	67°
Use. For plumbers' wiped joints and outdoor work because lead weathers well.					
Blowpipe solder	40	60	183°C.	230°C.	47°
Use. General benchwork—hand soldering with copper bit and blowpipe.					
Tinsmiths' fine work	60	40	183°C.	188°C.	5°
Use. A free-running solder for fine work such as in radio and television sets.					

Soldering requires heat, but every time we heat metal the oxygen in the air attacks the metal surface, forming an oxide. This oxide is a hard thin skin which prevents the solder coming in contact with the actual metal, and must be got rid of. First the metal is cleaned to get rid of existing oxides, dirt and grease by means of a smooth file and clean emery cloth. It is then coated along the surfaces to be joined with a flux of some sort.

The purpose of the flux is to dissolve the oxides which form on the joint when heat is applied and render them fluid, and also to dissolve the oxide on the solder so as to let it run freely along the joint and alloy with the parent metal. The word 'flux' is of foreign origin and means 'to flow'.

Fluxes are of two kinds, (a) those which chemically clean the surface of the metal, i.e. they are 'active' fluxes, and (b) those which protect the surface only. Of the two, (a) is the better and easier to work with, but after soldering care must be taken to rinse the work in running water to prevent the corrosive action of the flux destroying the joint and damaging the metal. Fluxes under (b) are best used on small work such as wire jointing and work which has already been tinned.

ZINC CHLORIDE (Known also as 'Killed spirits')

This is a popular and very widely used flux. It can be made quite easily by placing snippings of zinc in a glass jar of hydrochloric acid.

The zinc should be added until all action ceases, when the acid is said to be killed, and the liquid is then known as zinc chloride or killed spirits.

This liquid is corrosive and care must be taken to wash any joint after soldering with this flux. Killed spirits is used principally on steel, copper and brass work, but owing to its corrosive properties it is never used on electrical work.

RESIN

This is a good flux for brass and electrical work, being non-corrosive. A popular form of soft solder has a core of resin through the centre of its entire length. Care must be taken to clean the joint thoroughly because this flux is protective only, though an activated resin is now on the market.

Cleanliness at all times is essential, for even the perspiration from one's fingers is sufficient to make soldering difficult if not impossible.

TALLOW AND CANDLEGREASE

These are both good fluxes with soft solders having a high lead content. Candlegrease is particularly good on lead pipe work, while tallow rubbed on tinplate cleans and fluxes the surface ready for soldering.

SAL-AMMONIAC (or Ammonium Chloride)

A useful flux with solders having a high tin content. It is also used for the tinning of copperwork and cleaning the copper bit.

Two popular patent fluxes on the market are 'Bakers Fluid' and 'Fluxite'. Both are corrosive and joints must be well washed after soldering.

COPPER BIT OR SOLDERING IRON, Fig. 111

Use. For applying heat and soft solder to metal.

Parts. 1. Copper head or bolt
    2. Mild steel shank
    3. Wooden handle
} Riveted or screwed and pinned in the shank which in turn is secured in the wooden handle.

The bit is available in many sizes denoted by a number which indicates the weight of the head in grammes and ranges from No. 2 to No. 12, though much heavier heads are available for special work. Soldering bits are usually straight or hatchet shaped but a variety of 'irons' of different shapes should be made and collected to suit the various jobs that come along.

Copper is used for the bit because it takes in heat quickly, gives heat out quickly, and it has an affinity for soft solder.

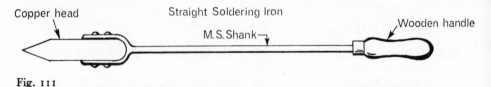

Copper head   Straight Soldering Iron   Wooden handle

M. S. Shank

Fig. 111

SOLDERING STOVES, Fig. 112

These are used for heating the copper bits. A useful guide for determining the correct heat is to note the instant a green flame appears, for that indicates the iron is ready for use. It helps if two irons are used, so that there is no waiting, one iron heating while the other is in use. At the first sign of pastiness of the solder, the iron should be changed for a hot one. The use of emery cloth and file to finish off a soldered joint is to be strongly deprecated. It shows inability to solder, wastes time, weakens an already badly made joint, and spoils the emery cloth and file used.

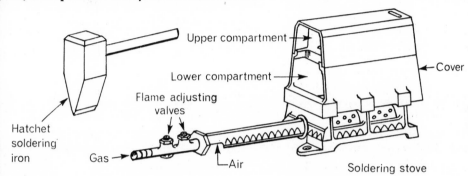

Fig. 112

TINNING THE BIT

To solder with the bit demands that it be 'tinned'. That is, a large area of the end is coated with soft solder as follows so that it appears like a piece of tinplate.

1. If the bit is in a bad condition it should be filed first to present a clean smooth surface of copper.

2. Heat the bit in the bottom half of the stove, which should be adjusted to give a slightly oxidizing flame.

3. When a green flame appears, withdraw the bit and quickly dip it in a basin of killed spirits to dissolve the oxides.

4. The cleaned copper is touched with a piece of soft solder which will flow over the hot clean metal and form a silvery coating of 'wet' solder.

The bit is now tinned and when used for a properly prepared and fluxed joint should be placed on one end and held still for about five seconds to give the heat time to flow into the work. The solder will then flow into the joint and the bit should be slowly drawn along the work causing the liquid solder to flow from the bit to the heated metal where it will push away the molten oxide and alloy with the hot parent metal, Fig. 113.

Having tinned the bit, it need only be cleaned from time to time by dipping it in a small tin of sal-ammoniac. Constant dipping in the zinc chloride should be avoided as this results in a very dirty flux.

Where possible, soft soldering should be carried out using a small torch or blow pipe.

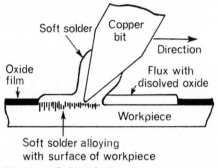

Fig. 113 Soft soldering

This method is much easier than using a soldering iron and results in a much neater job. The heat supply is constant and adequate and the solder runs freely without having to be drawn along with the bit which always leaves evidence of its movement.

Tinning is not confined to the soldering iron but may also be carried out on most metals. This process is most useful for the soldering together of areas of metal as it ensures complete coverage all over the inside of the joint, examples being the joining together of two washers and the repair of a container by using a thin metal disc.

Tinning is carried out by either (a) drawing a hot tinned bit across the surface of the metal or (b) laying a small bead of solder on the metal and warming it up when the solder will flow. It may be necessary to assist it to flow using a piece of wire to spread it evenly over the surface. To unite the two pieces of tinned metal they should be lightly fluxed, placed together and warmed with a soft flame when solder will be seen to 'sweat' at the joint indicating it has melted, Fig. 114. Sometimes it may be necessary to move the top piece of work slightly with the wire just to ensure that melting has taken place. A clean joint can be made by wiping quickly round the edges with an old small brush dipped in flux.

The jointing together of two tinned surfaces is known as 'sweating', and may be described as a soft solder sandwich. All work done in tinplate is best done with the copper bit as so little heat must be used to avoid damage to the work, so when sweating it is sufficient to lay the hot bit on the parts to be joined.

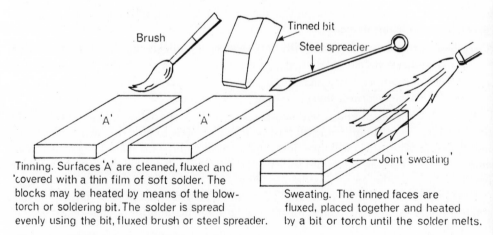

Tinning. Surfaces 'A' are cleaned, fluxed and 'covered with a thin film of soft solder. The blocks may be heated by means of the blow-torch or soldering bit. The solder is spread evenly using the bit, fluxed brush or steel spreader.

Sweating. The tinned faces are fluxed, placed together and heated by a bit or torch until the solder melts.

Fig. 114 Tinning and sweating

Tinning and sweating is also carried out when assembling rings and bushes on tubes, and to enable the solder to flow properly in the joint a clearance of about 0.1 mm to 0.2 mm should be aimed at.

Aluminium cannot be soft soldered with normal equipment due to the oxide film forming faster than the flux can destroy it.

Hard soldering

Hard soldering is the joining together of metals by means of a solder consisting of copper, zinc and silver which melts and alloys with the parent metals when they are made red hot.

The proportions of the metals used to make the hard solders vary to give different strengths, melting points, flowing qualities and plastic ranges. Because of the addition of silver these solders are often known as silver solders, and their melting points range from about 610°C. to 850°C., the former temperature being at a dull red heat. The following table gives details of four popular solders which are some of many made by Johnson, Matthey and Co. Ltd.

EASY-FLO NO. 2

42 per cent silver, the remainder brass with a little cadmium. Melting range 608°C. to 617°C. Good fitting joints are necessary. The solder is quick flowing and gives a smooth ductile joint.

ARGO-SWIFT

29 per cent silver, the remainder brass with a little cadmium. Melting range is 607°C. to 700°C., giving a long plastic range. This solder is useful where wide gaps occur, or where pronounced fillets are required.

G-6

67 per cent silver, the remainder brass. The melting range is 705°C. to 723°C. This solder is good for general usage. It is a white coloured solder and particularly valued for this reason by the silversmith.

C4

24 per cent silver, the remainder brass. The melting range is 740°C. to 780°C. This solder is popular as the first step in two-stage soldering when followed by Easy-flo No. 2.

These solders are available in the form of long rods, wire, strip and foil, and have a high tensile strength being around 5 tonnes per square cm for Easy-flo No. 2.

This higher range of temperature means that a blow torch of some kind must be used. The forge fire is useful for large work but control is difficult, and for most work a blow torch connected to the gas mains and a double-acting bellows or small air compressor to supply the air to the flame is simpler, cleaner and more convenient. A paraffin blowlamp

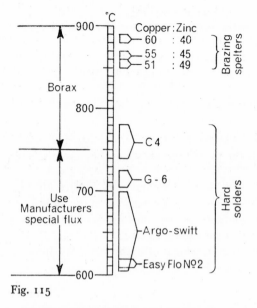

Fig. 115

is also very good but not quite so convenient as the blow torch.

As in soft soldering the parts to be joined must be cleaned to expose clean metal, a piece of emery cloth or a smooth file being suitable for the job. There are two fluxes available and care must be taken to choose the right one. It is important that the flux melts at a much lower temperature than the solder, to ensure a completely liquid flux. The melting point of borax is around 650°C., so it can only be used with safety on hard solders whose melting points are about 750°C. and above. For hard solders which melt below 750°C. special patent fluxes are used, and are obtainable from the manufacturers of the hard solders, Fig. 115.

Having selected the hard solder, the correct flux is chosen and mixed with just sufficient water to give a creamy consistency. The joint is carefully painted with the prepared flux using a thin camel hair brush, or the flattened end of a piece of thin wire.

The important part of hard soldering is to get the joint red hot, otherwise the solder will not flow. To do this the work must be mounted on firebricks or small pieces of coke

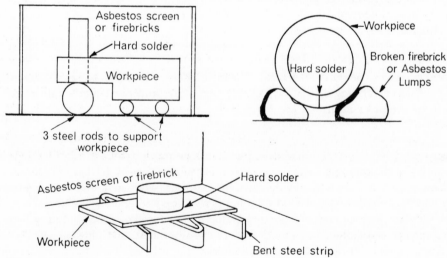

Fig. 116 Mounting of work for heating

with firebricks, and with asbestos screens placed behind and at the sides of the work to reflect heat, Fig. 116.

A small piece of solder is now placed on the joint and the work raised to a red heat by first applying a medium hard flame and moving it about to prevent local heating, warping and twisting. The torch should be held in the left hand by a right-handed person leaving the right hand free for manipulating the solder or a wire prodder as work proceeds. When the work is hot, a smaller slightly oxidizing flame is directed on the actual joint.

The flux will at first bubble and swell then settle down and melt. Next, the pellet of solder will melt into a ball, then when the joint is red hot (the degree of heat depending upon the grade of solder) the solder will flow along the joint. If desired, no solder need be applied to the joint in the first instance, but the work heated up just as before until it is red hot when the joint is touched with the end of the solder previously dipped in flux. Solder will flow into the joint and flow towards the hottest part of the work so that it can be drawn along by heating just in front of it. Either method may be employed, each has its points, and there are occasions when one is preferable to the other. On small joints and fine work it may be desirable to apply a small pellet of solder, while on long joints it is often better to feed the solder on from the end of a rod.

The 'prodder' mentioned above is easily made from a 250 mm length of 3 mm diameter steel rod. One end is bent to form a loop for a handle while the other end is hammered flat and filed to a spearlike point. When this tool is drawn along a molten joint, especially a fillet, it results in a superior finish. Sometimes the solder 'hangs up' and refuses to run, when this happens a light tap with the prodder quickly sets it going.

The parts to be joined must be a good close fit, cleaned and in close metallic contact. A small V groove on the inside of joints in metal more than 3 mm thick adds to the strength of the joint.

Because of the tendency of work to warp and twist when two or more pieces have to be assembled it is necessary to fasten work together, usually by means of soft iron binding wire about 1 mm in diameter. The wire is fastened round the work with a loop at the middle and a twist at its ends. Tightening is effected by twisting the loop and the ends by means of flat-nosed pliers. Always twist in a clockwise direction, so that if several wires need to be adjusted, confusion won't arise as to which way to turn each loop, Fig. 117.

Patent fluxes are purchased as a powder in tins and are quite simple to use. Borax is obtainable in several shapes and forms. Normally it is in the form of a white powder but may be in the form of a cone known as a jewellers' cone.

Brazing

Brazing is the soldering together of metals using a brass often referred to as SPELTER, which was the old name for zinc.

Brazing is carried out in exactly the same way as hard soldering, excepting that higher

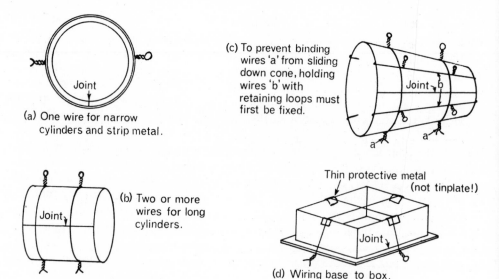

(a) One wire for narrow cylinders and strip metal.

(b) Two or more wires for long cylinders.

(c) To prevent binding wires 'a' from sliding down cone, holding wires 'b' with retaining loops must first be fixed.

Thin protective metal (not tinplate!)

(d) Wiring base to box.

(e) Wiring base to cylinder. The base is cut out roughly octagonal to keep binding wire in position, then cut and filed to size after soldering.

(f) Use of split pins to fix narrow strip to component.

Fig. 117   Wiring up joints

temperatures are necessary. These range from about 850°C. to over 1000°C. depending on the composition of the spelter, Fig. 115. Again, the secret of good, quick brazing lies in the arrangement of firebricks and asbestos screens to conserve and reflect heat upon the joint. This may take some time and tax one's ingenuity, but in view of the high temperature required it is time well spent. In fact, large work often demands much care, thought and skill at this stage to make brazing possible at all. Small articles, especially those in copper, should be supported at three or four points only so as to make as little contact with the surface of other materials as possible. This is because copper takes in heat quickly and also gives it out quickly, and if laid flat on a firebrick, just would not get hot until the whole area was at red heat.

THE FLAME

When a flame is used without any air pressure it will be seen to be 'soft', large and mainly yellow in colour. This is known as a carburizing flame and is useless for heating purposes. As air pressure is increased the flame gradually turns purple-blue in colour and becomes 'harder', that is, it becomes rigid and is not so easily blown to one side.

From the blow torch nozzle the first one-third length of the flame consists of a thin envelope of burning gas enclosing a long cone of air, but from the middle to the end of the flame the burning gas and air combine and better combustion takes place. It is in this part of the flame that the heat is to be found and a rough guide is to use that part of the flame about two-thirds of the way from the torch nozzle.

A REDUCING FLAME is one in which there is unburnt gas because of an insufficient supply of air and this type of flame is usually luminous. A NEUTRAL flame is one in which the gas is just burnt by virtue of enough air supply. This type of flame is dark in colour, and both the gas and the oxygen in the air are burnt. An OXIDISING FLAME is one in which there is an excessive air supply and is usually dark-coloured and very noisy. The surplus oxygen then attacks the metal, forming oxides and blowholes which are damaging and wasteful. The correct flame to use for soldering is very slightly oxidizing.

Double-acting bellows were a satisfactory method of supplying air to the blow torch but the use of natural gas requires a small air compressor. This is driven off the electric mains but is best housed in a separate room or store as compressors are noisy in use. When using compressed air, no matter how low the pressure, it must never be allowed to blow near the eyes, ears, nose or mouth, because of the serious internal injuries which may result therefrom.

12

Beaten Metalwork

Ancient civilizations developed the art of beaten metalwork to a high standard. The royal cemetery at Ur and Egyptian tombs have revealed gold and silver objects showing that these early craftsmen were experts at nearly all the hand processes we know today including the inlaying of bronze work with gold and silver.

Later, these skills spread to Greece where, during the sixth to second centuries B.C. the art of the goldsmith reached a standard of skill, beauty and delicacy which has never been excelled.

Beaten metalwork is the art of shaping a thin piece of malleable metal by striking it all over using a hammer or mallet and a suitable support or stake. Because the surface finish of the metal is very important hammers and stakes should be smooth and bright otherwise imperfections will be repeatedly stamped on the workpiece as shaping proceeds. The common hammers and mallets are shown in Fig. 118.

Silver is an excellent material with which to work, but its high cost prohibits its general use. Copper is very good, possessing a high malleable quality and having a rich, warm colour. The metal, however, is soft and in built-up work which cannot be finally

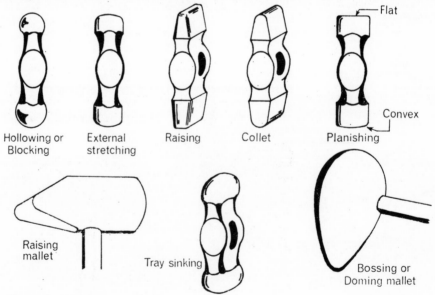

Hollowing or Blocking

External stretching

Raising

Collet

Planishing — Flat — Convex

Raising mallet

Tray sinking

Bossing or Doming mallet

Fig. 118   Hammers and Mallets

hardened by planishing, the article may lose its shape if carelessly handled before it has age hardened. Gilding metal is the most popular metal for this class of work, having a rich golden colour and being only slightly less malleable than copper. This is more than balanced by its hardness, which imparts firmness to the finished item. Brass can be used, but its low melting point limits the variety of soldering it can take, while its hardness makes it less easy to work.

Constant hammering hardens the metal, not only making it difficult to work but increasing the risk of cracks developing. A good general rule therefore is to put the metal through the following annealing routine before starting and subsequently after every second all-over hammering:

1. Anneal the metal.
2. Immerse in an acid bath for about five minutes, using copper or brass tongs only.
3. Remove and rinse in running water.
4. Dry in sawdust or with clean rag.
5. Clean both sides using pumice powder and a fine brass wire scratch brush.
6. Remove any scratches by rubbing with a stick of Water of Ayr stone and water.

The metal is now prepared ready for working.

The acid, or pickle, is made by slowly adding one volume of sulphuric acid to about seven volumes of water in an earthenware or lead-lined bath. Steel tongs ought not to be used because they affect the acid causing copper to be deposited on gilding metal and brass articles pickled later. The purpose of the pickling is to remove the black oxide scale after annealing.

SHAPING

The three principal methods of shaping are Hollowing, Sinking and Raising. In each method it is essential to develop a rhythmic action to produce evenly shaped work. Throughout, the left hand has to exert considerable pressure to hold the workpiece steady against the force of hammering. One complete all-over hammering is known as a Course.

Sandbag

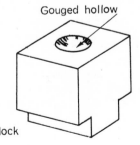

Gouged hollow

Wood block

Fig. 119

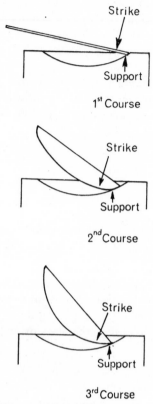

Strike

Support

1st Course

Strike

Support

2nd Course

Strike

Support

3rd Course

Fig. 120   Hollowing

HOLLOWING

This is shaping by stretching and thinning, the metal being struck on the inside just beyond the point of contact. For discs over, say, 120 mm diameter, a sandbag support is required, but for sizes below this, a hardwood block with a shallow hollow in the end grain should be used, Fig. 119.

The prepared disc is marked out with pencilled guide lines about 10 mm apart. The disc is firmly held in the left hand with the rim on the support, and hollowing begins by striking the metal with a doming mallet just beyond the point of support so that the metal is depressed into the space behind, Fig. 120. For small work a hollowing or blocking hammer is used instead

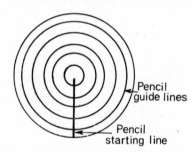

Pencil
guide lines

Pencil
starting line

of the doming mallet. The first circle of malleting is completed by slightly rotating the workpiece anti-clockwise after each blow. Hollowing proceeds circle by circle from the rim to the centre when the shape is tested by sighting the bowl in line with the stake upon which it is to be finished, Fig. 121. Should the metal twist or buckle it must be corrected at once by pressing it over the edge of the bench. This process of hollowing continues until the bowl is slightly more concave than is required for the stake to allow for stretching.

Pencilled guide lines are now set out on the outside of the bowl which is trued up and

Fig. 121   Sighting

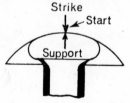

Strike

Start

Support

Fig. 122   Smoothing

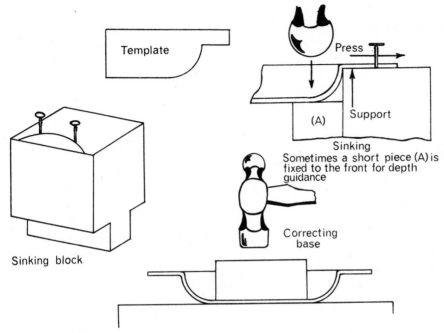

Template

Press

(A)   Support

Sinking

Sometimes a short piece (A) is
fixed to the front for depth
guidance

Correcting
base

Sinking block

Fig. 123   Sinking

made smooth all over by malleting on the stake working in circles from the bowl centre outwards. A hide mallet is used and the blows are delivered over the same spot on the stake throughout while the workpiece is rotated clockwise, Fig. 122. The bowl should now be of the correct shape, smooth and ready for planishing.

HOLLOWING BY SINKING, Fig. 123

This method is used to produce trays and similar forms. The prepared disc has the sinking line marked out, and by resting it on the end grain of a hardwood block, the position can be found for two wire nails required to support the rim. The disc is placed on the wood and thrust firmly back against the two nails while a blocking or a tray sinking hammer is used to sink the metal by striking just beyond the sinking line. Several complete rotations of hammering will be necessary before the required depth is reached and a template should be used to check this. When distortion occurs, the metal must be carefully trued up before proceeding.

Small hollowed forms, suitable for use as domed feet, can be worked in a steel doming block using round nosed punches. These small shapes can also be made by means of steel punches on a lead block.

RAISING

Most first-class work is shaped by raising, which contracts the metal by striking it on the outside just beyond the point of contact. Thinning is avoided, in fact the metal is often made thicker at the rim of the finished object. There are two methods of raising, (a) mallet and (b) hammer.

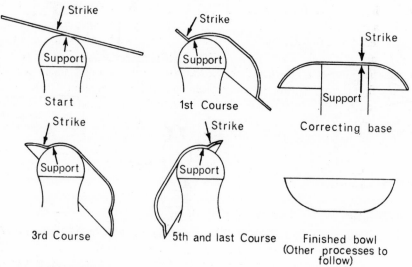

Fig. 124   Mallet raising

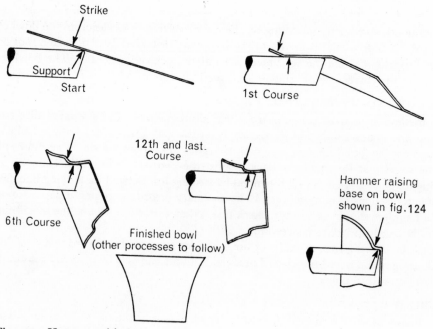

Fig. 125   Hammer raising

RAISING WITH THE MALLET, Fig. 124

This method is more suitable for wider, shallow forms. Dome and ball stakes are used, the latter being necessary for deeper shapes. The boxwood mallet should be wedge shaped with a rounded face.

The prepared disc is marked out to show the base circle and guide lines 10 mm apart, then held firmly at a slight angle with the base circle on the stake. The metal is struck just beyond the point of contact and rotated anti-clockwise slightly after each blow to complete the first circle resulting in a step right round the workpiece. The second circle is struck on the rise of the step and beyond the new point of contact with the stake so as to work the metal downward and forward circle by circle to the rim. After the first course, the result will be a shallow raised dish. The complete operation is repeated until the correct shape is obtained. Occasionally the flat base should be trued up on the end of a round bar. During the later courses it is often more convenient to reverse the work and strike from the near side.

RAISING WITH THE HAMMER, Fig. 125

This method is quicker than the mallet and suitable for tall objects such as vases, but the metal is subject to marking from the constant hammering.

The prepared disc is marked out, base circle and guide lines 6 mm apart, then held at a slight angle with the base circle on the end of the raising stake. Hammering begins just beyond the point of contact depressing the metal down through the space to just touch the stake. When the first full circle has been hammered, a step will have been formed right round the metal. Raising proceeds by hammering the rise of this step downward and forward one circle at a time to the rim. After the first few circles have been worked, it is advisable to move the workpiece back off the end of the stake to avoid damage to the base. Raising continues, course by course, until the desired form has been reached. As

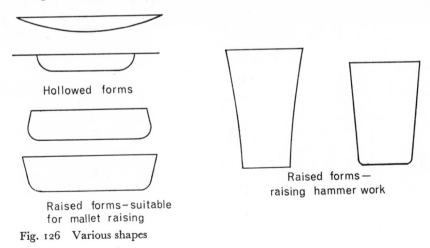

Hollowed forms

Raised forms — suitable for mallet raising

Fig. 126   Various shapes

Raised forms — raising hammer work

113

with the malleting method, the base should be regularly trued up on the end of a round bar. Typical shapes which can be made using these three methods are shown in Fig. 126.

PLANISHING, Fig. 127

Planishing is the final hammering stage and serves three purposes:

1. To smooth the metal.
2. To correct the shape.
3. To harden the metal.

The blows are delivered from the wrist so as to fall lightly on the work and directly on the point of contact with the stake. Guide lines should be used and every part of the metal covered by the hammer. Planishing is best done twice, the first time using a direct straight tap and the second time using a glancing tap to impart a better finish.

The convex face of the planishing hammer is applied to flat surfaces and the flat face to convex surfaces to avoid unsightly hammer marks. The surface of the workpiece can never be better than the tools being used and for this reason the surfaces of the stake and planishing hammer must be mirror bright.

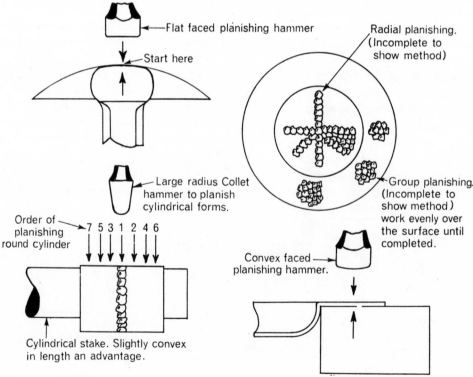

Fig. 127　Planishing

The three methods of planishing are (a) circular, (b) group, (c) radial. Circular planishing is the more general and is applied to the outside of medium and small-sized bowls working from the centre in circles to the rim. Group planishing is applied to large work and tray rims, the planish marks being in clusters of a dozen or so. Radial planishing is applied to flat circular tray bases to avoid distortion. It must be emphasized that the purpose of planishing is not to put a pretty pattern on the object.

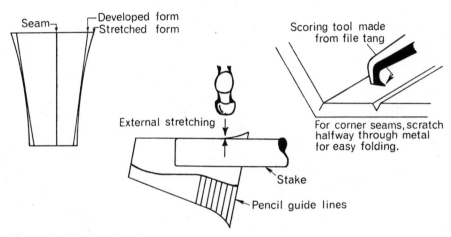

Fig. 128   Developed work

SEAMED WORK

A quick and simple method of producing cylindrical and cone forms is to bend the developed shape round a stake and hard solder the seam. The correct profile is then obtained by hammering on suitable stakes, Fig. 128. Provided the seam is well made this method is quite acceptable except for first-class work. Difficulty arises if the finished article consists of several pieces soldered together, the seamed joints then adding to the problem of soldering by increasing the number of stages.

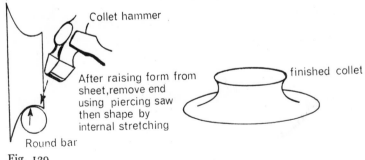

Fig. 129

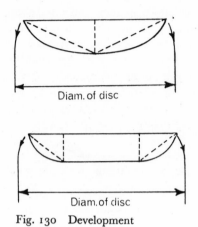

Fig. 130   Development

On small work, the base can be made from a strip of, say, 6 mm by 1.5 mm gilding metal, bent to a circular form and soldered. This is then soldéred to the bowl using a lower grade melting point solder. On larger good-class work the base or collet, would be raised from a flat disc, its base would then be removed by piercing saw and the shape finally produced by stretching, Fig. 129.

The diameter of the required disc for hollowed ware is found by striking arcs from the curve base as shown. It is usual to add 3 mm to this size to allow for final trimming. With raising, a smaller disc is required than for hollowing due to the 'growth' of the height due to contraction. On shallow bowls this is negligible, but quite considerable on tall narrow forms, Fig. 130.

WIRES AND MOULDINGS

In all but the smallest work, the thin edges should be strengthened and supported in some way. One method is to work a narrow lip of the rim over to form a beaded edge, but a more pleasing way is to apply ornamental wire or strip in copper or gilding metal.

After cutting to length and shaping it is held in place by means of split pins and soldered to the workpiece. Copper wires can be twisted to give a ropelike effect using the vice and hand drill. The result can be tapped slightly flat for a different shape and to increase the soldering area. Other designs can be made such as plaiting various numbers of wires, or simply twisting square strip to get a 'barley sugar' effect, Fig. 131.

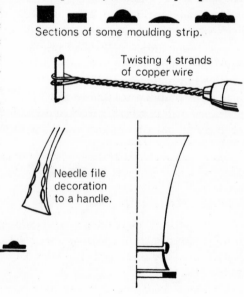

Sections of some moulding strip.

Twisting 4 strands of copper wire

Needle file decoration to a handle.

Decorative wires and strip.

Fig. 131   Edge treatment

POLISHING

Metal is polished by straight-line rubbing with various abrasives, working from the coarse to the fine.

Emery

This is obtainable in many grits from oo (known as two nought and written 2/o) to No. 6, the coarsest, in strip form or sheet with paper or cloth backing. Blue backed emery is obtainable as fine as 4/o, while crocus cloth, the finest, is used for very fine polishing of beaten metalwork and the maintenance of hammer faces and stakes.

Pumice powder

This is ground from pumice stone (a product of volcanic eruptions) and has good abrasive qualities.

Water of Ayr stone

A slatelike stone used in stick form for the removal of small scratches by rubbing along their length. Ideal on copper, brass and aluminium.

Whiting

A powdered chalk having a fine polishing action. Useful on tinplate work.

Polishing machine

Calico mops are used on the grindstone extension spindle for the polishing of metal. Buffing soap, consisting of a fine abrasive mixed with wax is used for polishing which should take place across the remaining scratches. For final polishing, a lambs' wool mop with a little jewellers' rouge is used. Hold the work in the hands only, and apply the lower half of the work to the lower half of the mop.

Liquid metal polish

These are obtainable with a fast abrasive action for brasswork and a mild action for valuable metals such as silver. The metal is well rubbed with the correct liquid, then polished with a clean rag.

   The successful cleaning and polishing of work depends upon keeping the various mops and cloths to their respective abrasives.

METAL FINISHING

Wrought ironwork should have loose scale removed, after which it can be given a coat of metal priming paint followed by a coat of black undercoat or black eggshell gloss. Some general metalwork items can be protected with a coat of acetate paint as used by model makers.

   Steel tools in regular use only require wiping with an oily rag. Some tools can be heated to a brown-purple colour then wiped or dipped in linseed oil. With beaten metal-

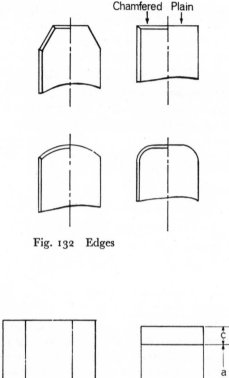

Fig. 132   Edges

Trinket box 3 : 1

Fig. 133   Proportion

work, washing in hot soapy water followed by wax polishing produces a mellow tone lasting several months, but for a more durable finish lacquer must be applied. Because it is quick drying this is best done by a specialist firm, otherwise a thick treacle-like finish results. A better method which can be done in the workshop is to apply a coat of transparent polyurethane varnish which gives a thin clear coat and has a drying time of about $1\frac{1}{2}$ hours. Best results are obtained by thinning the varnish with turpentine.

Design

Design means everything which goes into the making of anything and includes size, shape, construction, material, colour and finish, so that the end-product is exactly suitable for its purpose.

Shape is important, and to be interesting the eye must be shown something which it does not readily analyse. For this reason rectangles are preferable to monotonous squares, and the sides should be in the proportion of 1 : 2, 1 : 3, 2 : 3, or some such definite ratio. The Greeks liked the proportion 5 : 8 so much that they called it the 'Golden Oblong'. The heavy appearance of metal can often be lessened by shaping or removing the corners and filing chamfers along some or all of the edges, Fig. 132.

With the division of large areas, like fire screens and gates, the central unit should be greater than the side units to avoid a 'squashed in' appearance, while the raising of the central unit slightly above the middle avoids a 'heavy' look and suggests lightness, Fig. 133.

The circle is a dull shape, but by breaking it up into an odd number of units interest is captured, and the rim of a small bowl, divided into three, five or seven equal parts by means of punches, takes on a pleasing form, Fig. 134. A large bowl with a built-up rim must be left circular, but in this case the bowl profile should be the main attraction.

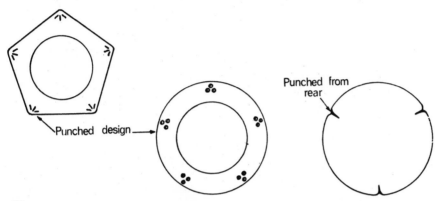

Fig. 134

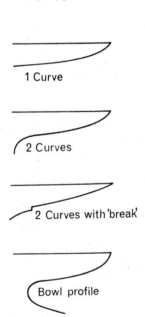

1 Curve

2 Curves

2 Curves with 'break'

Bowl profile

Fig. 135

Curves following an elliptical line are much more desirable than those struck from compasses, and where two such curves join they should flow in opposite directions with one smaller than the other. The profiles of bowls and wrought iron scrolls ought to follow these lines for maximum eye appeal, Fig. 135.

If a tall column having parallel sides is viewed from a distance the sides appear concave. This is an optical illusion which the Greeks overcame when building their temples by slightly swelling the middles of the columns, a practice known as ENTASIS. For this reason when designing items such as standard lamps some feature must be worked in the centre, Fig. 136.

Before starting to design, get to know the different metals in general use in the workshop, their characteristics and properties, and their sizes and shapes. Know the ways in which each can be worked, their limitations and the various ways by which they can be joined.

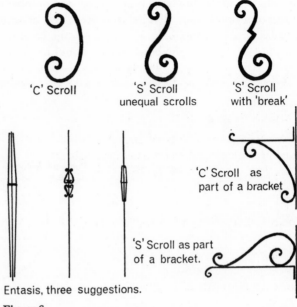

'C' Scroll

'S' Scroll
unequal scrolls

'S' Scroll
with 'break'

'C' Scroll as
part of a bracket

'S' Scroll as part
of a bracket.

Entasis, three suggestions.

Fig. 136

When designing, crystallize your ideas on paper, making a number of rough sketches. Study these carefully, altering and adjusting where necessary until the final result is pleasing to look at and possible to make. Before starting work, see all the tools are available, making any special items such as, for example, hammers and stakes for beaten metalwork.

I3

Clamps, Gauges and Micrometers

TOOLMAKERS' CLAMP, Fig. 137

Use. For clamping two or more pieces of metal together. Several clamps are often used when assembling sheet and strip.

Parts. 1. Jaws, mild steel, casehardened.
2. Screws, mild steel.
3. Clip, mild steel. The clip prevents the jaws dropping together.

For gripping, the centre screw must be tightened first, and finally the end screw to get extra 'purchase'.

The tool is obtained singly, a pair of clamps being two tools.

Tool makers' clamp

Fig. 137

V BLOCKS, Fig. 138

Use. For supporting cylindrical work during marking out and when machining.

V blocks are generally made of cast iron and consist of an accurately machined block with opposite sides parallel and adjacent faces square to each other. A 90° angled V groove of different size is machined along two opposite faces with a small clearance groove in the bottom corner of each. V blocks are normally made in pairs and care should be taken to use the correct pair. Slots along the sides of the block enable special clamps to be used for locating and holding work securely.

V block

Fig. 138

THE SURFACE PLATE, Fig. 139

Use. 1. For comparing the flatness of surfaces.
2. For providing a plane surface from which to measure, test and mark out.

Material. Cast iron.

Cast iron is chosen because of its great rigidity. Webs are arranged in the casting for lightness and strength and three feet enable the smaller surface plates to remain

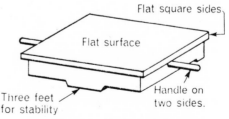

Flat square sides

Flat surface

Three feet for stability

Handle on two sides.

Fig. 139   Surface plate

E

stable even though the bench may be uneven.

After machining the surface plate as flat and true as possible it is allowed to 'season' to ensure that there are no stresses which will cause the metal to move out of shape when finished. It is then scraped by hand to a dead flat surface, using another surface plate as a means of testing. The edges are generally machined and scraped true and square to the surface to increase the scope of the work which may be undertaken.

SURFACE GAUGE, Fig. 140

Use.   1. For testing and setting work in the lathe.
   2. For marking scribed lines on work parallel to the surface plate.
   3. For measuring and testing heights.

Parts.   1. Base, cast iron, or case hardened steel, or hardened steel.
   2. Rocker arm and adjusting screw.
   3. Spindle clamp, spring loaded.
   4. Spindle.
   5. Scriber clamp, spring loaded.
   6. Scriber.

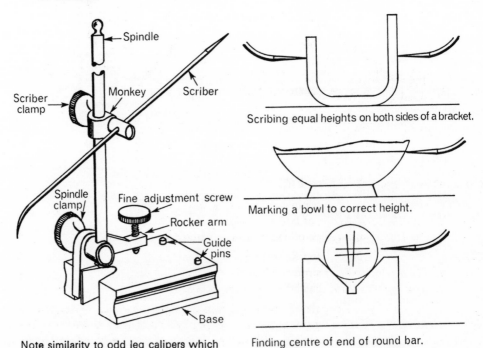

Scribing equal heights on both sides of a bracket.

Marking a bowl to correct height.

Finding centre of end of round bar.
Set scriber to approximate centre.
Scribe bar end in four positions.

Note similarity to odd leg calipers which work from edge whereas surface gauge works from an area.

Fig. 140   Surface gauge

The surface gauge in its simplest form consists of a block of steel for a base with a length of 6 mm or 8 mm diameter rod screwed in the middle. On this rod is a scriber clamp, often called a 'monkey'. This is free to move up and down the spindle and can be locked in any position when it also secures the scriber rigidly.

This instrument is often referred to as a scribing block, which in fact it is, being simply a scriber held on a block, comparable to the odd leg calipers in that a scriber is rigidly held and guided. The scope of the scriber is increased by having one end curved and the other end straight, so enabling perpendicular contact in awkward places.

In use, the scriber is first set to the approximate size or position. The exact size is then obtained by means of the fine adjusting screw working the rocker arm. For moving the gauge parallel to an edge or slot two frictionally held pins are mounted in the base and only need pushing down to bring them into use.

When setting the surface gauge to a particular height, a rule must be used together with a try square or angle plate to ensure that the rule is vertical.

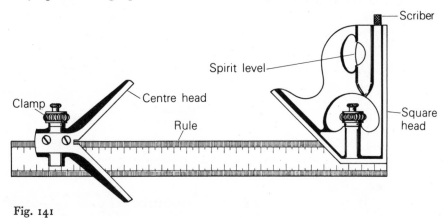

Fig. 141

COMBINATION SQUARE, Fig. 141

Use. 1. For measuring and testing right angles, and 45° angles.
2. For checking depths of holes.
3. For finding the centre of the end of a round bar.

Parts. 1. The square head, drop forged steel.
2. The centre head, drop forged steel.
3. Rule, carbon steel, hardened and tempered.

A groove runs along the middle of one side which engages with a spring-loaded pin in either of the heads for securing purposes. The square head is shaped to form a square at one side and a 45° angle at the other, and may be fixed to the rule to form a depth gauge or a try square.

The centre head when assembled with the rule forms a centre square, and can be used for locating the centre on the ends of round shafts. A line is scribed twice, using the tool in different positions. These lines are diameters so that their intersection gives the centre. A spirit level in the square head enables horizontal and vertical 'truing up' to be carried out to a high degree, while a small scriber contained in the end makes the combination square a compact and useful tool.

A protractor, graduated from 0° to 180°, is also available for clamping on the rule for use as a bevel or depth gauge. With the protractor the tool is known as a Combination Set.

ANGLE PLATE, Fig. 142

Use. 1. For securing work which cannot be held in lathe chucks or vices when machining.

2. For setting and securing work for testing and marking out on a surface plate.

Material. Cast iron, machined and ground to size and shape, and having flat faces and edges square to one another.

Angle plates are usually slotted in both faces to provide a means of bolting to the lathe faceplate or drilling machine table, and also for the bolting on of the work.

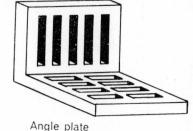

Angle plate

Fig. 142

BEVEL, Fig. 143

Use. For marking out angles and testing the angles of two adjacent faces.

Parts. 1. Stock, sometimes slotted, sometime having only a tapped hole in the simpler type.

2. Blade, straight or cranked and slotted along its length.

3. Recessed bolt and knurled nut for securing the parts together.

Material. Carbon steel, hardened and tempered, then ground true, straight and square, with parallel sides and edges.

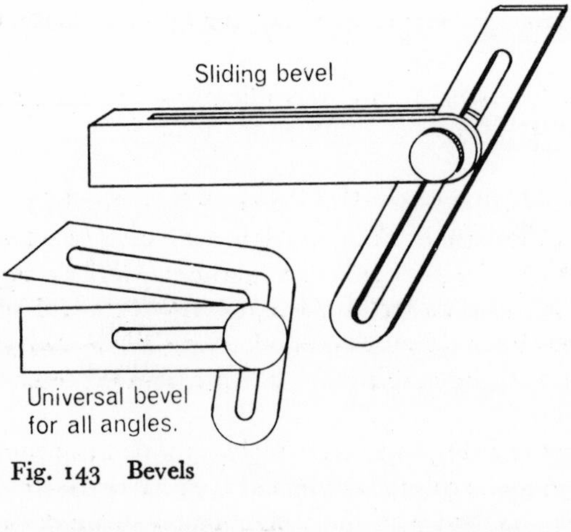

Sliding bevel

Universal bevel for all angles.

Fig. 143 **Bevels**

The plain bevel has a straight blade slotted to enable it to be slid about and rotated to any angle with the stock, while the universal bevel has a cranked blade with slot enabling a still greater variety of angles and testing to be carried out.

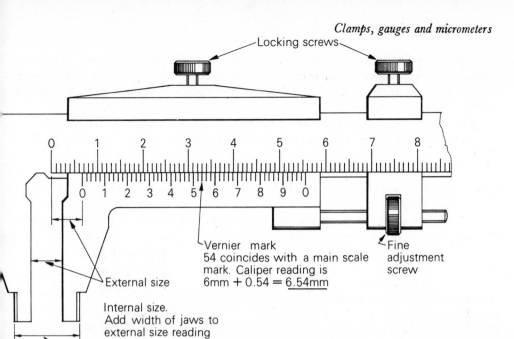

Locking screws

Vernier mark
54 coincides with a main scale
mark. Caliper reading is
6mm + 0.54 = 6.54mm

Fine
adjustment
screw

External size

Internal size.
Add width of jaws to
external size reading

THE VERNIER CALIPER GAUGE, Fig. 144

The vernier is a device for measuring small sizes accurately and is named after its inventor, Pierre Vernier. The parts are made of alloy or carbon steel, heat treated to resist wear and ground to a high degree of accuracy. As with all precision tools and gauges it should not be handled too much owing to the effects of expansion caused by the warmth of the hands. The correct temperature for accurate reading is 20°C, and this fact is usually engraved on the instrument.

By means of a vernier scale one is able to obtain a correct reading to a fine limit by noticing which line on a slide coincides exactly with any line on the main scale.

METRIC VERNIER CALIPER GAUGE, READING TO 0.1 MM, Fig. 145

A distance of 9 millimetres is marked on the vernier slide and this is divided into ten equal parts making each 0.9 mm long. When the jaws are closed the zero mark on the vernier is exactly opposite the zero mark on the main scale. The main scale is marked off in millimetres, but each division on the vernier is 0.9 mm, so that line one on the slide is 0.1 mm from the first millimetre division on the scale, line two is 0.2 mm from the second millimetre division, and so on.

If we move the vernier slide to the right to bring line one coincident with the 1 mm line on the main scale we must have moved the vernier 0.1 mm, and if we move the slide still further to the right to bring line two coincident with the 2 mm main scale mark we must have moved the vernier a total of 0.2 mm from the beginning. Thus, we have only to read off that vernier line number which coincides with a line on the main scale to get the number of 0.1 millimetres which have to be added to the initial reading. Fig. 146.

This is the type of gauge used in industry for good class work. The main scale is marked off in millimetres. A distance of 49 mm is marked on the vernier and this is divided into 50 equal parts making each 0.98 mm. A vernier division is therefore 0.02 mm short of a main scale division. To take a reading, first note the number of whole millimetres on the main scale up to the zero mark on the vernier. Then look along the vernier for the mark which is exactly in line with a main scale mark. Multiply 0.02 mm by this vernier mark number and add the result to the number of whole millimetres first noted to get the full reading. In practice it is usual to mark the vernier slide as shown so that the actual vernier reading is read at once without having to multiply.

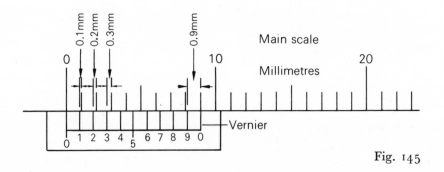

Fig. 145

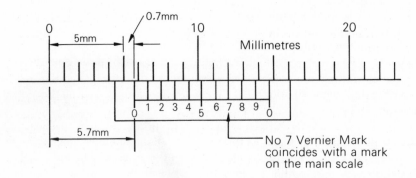

No 7 Vernier Mark coincides with a mark on the main scale

Fig. 146

Care must be taken never to force the vernier over the work for this will strain it and render it faulty. Nor must it ever be tried on work which is moving, as for example when turning in the lathe. The vernier caliper is light and compact and yet can be used to measure both internally and externally from zero to 150 mm in the smallest size, right up to a maximum of 1800 mm in the largest.

Fine adjustment is obtained by means of a small nut mounted on a screw fixed in the end of the sliding jaw.

The jaw tips, sometimes known as nibs, are made to an exact width and curved on the outsides for the measuring of holes. The width of the nibs is usually engraved on the jaw face and this size must be added to the reading when measuring internally. If in doubt, close the jaws to zero and measure them using another vernier or micrometer.

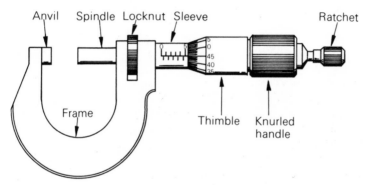

Fig. 147   Micrometer

THE MICROMETER, Fig. 147

The micrometer is an instrument used for measuring to a hundredth of a millimetre, and is operated by a screw. It is a more popular gauge than the vernier mainly because less eye strain is needed to read it. On the other hand, it is not such a versatile instrument as it will only perform one function, measuring either internally or externally, but not both. Even then its range is limited to within 25 mm or so unless a large frame is purchased, having a set of adjustable anvils.

The most popular of the micrometers is undoubtedly the outside type, having a capacity from zero to 25 mm. It consists of a sturdy U-shaped frame, one side of which contains the anvil and the other the spindle, the faces of these two parts being glass hard and flat. The spindle is threaded and fits in a main nut secured to the frame. A graduated sleeve covers this nut, and the thimble, secured to the end of the spindle, rotates freely over this sleeve. A lock nut or locking screw is fitted in the spindle when set to size. Sometimes a ratchet stop is fitted to the end of the spindle to ensure that the micrometer is not tightened too hard on the work.

The main screw has a pitch of 0.5 mm so that two complete turns of the thimble move the spindle 1 mm. Along the sleeve a datum line is marked off in half millimetres. For ease of reading whole millimetres are on one side of the line and half millimetres on the other. The thimble is marked off round its circumference into fifty equal divisions, each representing 1/50 of ½ mm which is 0.01 mm.

When reading a micrometer think of the size in three parts, writing down each and finally adding them up, though this may be done mentally later.

1. Note the number of whole millimetres.
2. Note if there is a half millimetre.
3. Multiply 0.01 mm by the thimble number reading.

The total gives the required reading.

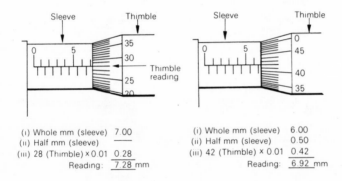

(i) Whole mm (sleeve)   7.00
(ii) Half mm (sleeve)   ——
(iii) 28 (Thimble) × 0.01   0.28
         Reading: 7.28 mm

(i) Whole mm (sleeve)   6.00
(ii) Half mm (sleeve)   0.50
(iii) 42 (Thimble) × 0.01   0.42
         Reading: 6.92 mm

Although it is necessary to use two hands on large micrometers, only one hand is required on the popular 25 mm size, Fig. 149. As with the vernier calipers, the micrometer must be used with care and not handled too often.

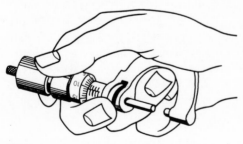

Before use, the accuracy of the vernier and micrometer should always be checked by closing the jaws lightly, when the reading should be zero. On some micrometers, adjustments can be made to make this so if error exists. Otherwise, the 'Zero error' as it is called, must be carefully noted, and either subtracted or added to the reading according as to whether the error is more or less than zero.

Fig. 149

128

FITTING. The making of a part to an exact size calls for great skill, takes time and is an expensive business. High speed mass production methods are made possible by allowing a small error in manufacture. This is done by giving each size two dimensions known as the *limits* so that if the part is made to any size within these limits the work is passed as correct. The narrow margin between the limits is called the *tolerance* and is very small in first class work.

Thus, instead of making a hole 25.00 mm diameter and a shaft 24.94 mm diameter to fit, it would be quicker to make the hole to any size from 25.00 mm to 25.02 mm and the shaft any size from 24.96 mm to 24.92 mm diameter. Not only does this method speed up the time of manufacture and so lower costs, but it also enables spare parts to be readily available as required.

14

The Lathe

A centre lathe, Fig. 150, is a machine tool used for machining cylinders, wheels, cones of various angles both internally and externally, and any combination of these shapes, machining the ends of metal flat and square to the main axis, and for cutting screw threads. The operation of machining metal in a lathe is known as turning.

The principle of the lathe is the removal of a volume of metal from a large area by rotating a cylinder against a tool moving slowly along it in a straight line.

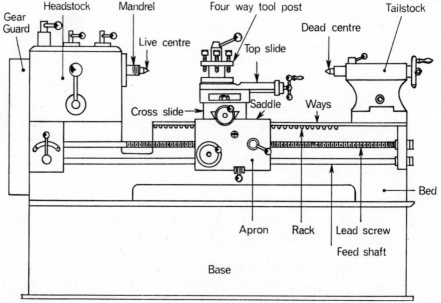

Fig. 150   A centre lathe

Parts of a lathe

BASE

The support upon which the lathe is secured. A sturdy well-braced bench, having a thick hardwood top suffices for small machines, but a steel cabinet built up, or fabricated by welding steel plates together, or a cast iron frame, is essential for most lathes, especially in the larger sizes.

BED

This is always made of cast iron because of its lack of tendency to bend, 'flow' or 'creep'.

WAYS

These are two machined and accurately scraped faces on top of the bed forming parallel guides for the carriage and tailstock.

CARRIAGE

This part consists essentially of two separate castings:

1. The Saddle, which is mounted on top of, and fitted to slide along, the ways.
2. The Apron, which is bolted to the front end of the saddle and hangs down in front of the bed. The apron is so placed as to conveniently house the various control wheels and levers to do with moving the carriage along the ways.

HEADSTOCK

This is the main casting at the left-hand end of the lathe and bolted to or forming part of the bed. Its purpose is to support the MAIN SPINDLE or MANDREL and the means by which this spindle is driven at various speeds.

Older lathes and most smaller ones usually have three or four stepped pulley cones cast in one piece, and sometimes referred to as speed cones. By means of a belt drive, various speeds are possible according to the diameter pulley on which the belt is running.

Modern lathes of the larger size, say 115 mm and over, now have all geared headstock, which means that the various spindle speeds are obtained by the selection and changing of gears using special levers.

MAIN SPINDLE OR MANDREL

This shaft is mounted in the headstock in two bearings, tapered roller bearings being superior to any others because of their accuracy and long life.

The mandrel is usually hollow, partly for economy of metal, weight and a saving in power, and also because it allows work to be entered well inside the chuck when turning the end of a long rod. It also permits the entry of a copper or brass rod at the far end for the removal of the lathe centre which can be fitted in the nose end of the mandrel. This nose has a screwed thread on the outside to take the various chucks, faceplate and driving plate, while the inside is tapered accurately to take the centre just mentioned.

TAILSTOCK

This is the casting at the right-hand end of the lathe ways. It is made in two parts: 1. the BASE, which is a sliding fit on the ways and capable of movement along them, and 2. the LOOSE HEAD or top piece which is accurately fitted to the base but may be adjusted sideways out of centre on either side of the main axis when it is desired to turn a taper.

A machined hollow spindle fits in the loosehead and is known as the BARREL or QUILL, the nose end being bored out and tapered to take a lathe centre. Often the outside of the quill is marked off in millimetres for convenience when drilling to certain depths. A clamping lever is fitted to one side so that the quill can be tightened up to remove 'play'.

By means of a handwheel, the quill may be wound in or out of the tailstock and the end of the threaded spindle which causes this movement very often acts as an ejector for the removal of the centre when the quill is screwed right back. The quill can also be used for holding various tools, including a drill chuck and morse tapered drills. A large clamping lever enables the tailstock to be firmly locked to the ways after sliding it to the desired position.

LEAD SCREW

This is the screwed shaft mounted in a bearing at each end on the front of the lathe. It passes right through the bearing at the left-hand end and is connected to the mandrel by means of a train of gear wheels which can be changed thus enabling screw threads of various pitches to be cut.

FEED SHAFT

Most lathes, and certainly those in the bigger sizes, are fitted with a feed shaft for the general everyday turning of metal by automatic means, leaving the lead screw solely for its important job of screw cutting.

This shaft is mounted parallel to the lead screw, passes behind the apron, and is securely housed in bearings at either end of the lathe. It is geared to the same train of gears as the lead screw shaft, thus providing a positive drive from the lathe mandrel. Behind the apron is mounted a worm, free to move along the shaft but made to rotate with it by means of a sliding key known as a feather. A lever on the apron front is used to engage this worm and its wheel in a train of gears and so give movement to the carriage.

THE GEARS

The gear wheels are mounted at the left-hand end of the lathe and should always be securely guarded. A set of change wheels is provided so that a variety of 'feeds' is obtainable.

RACK

A straight line of gear teeth bolted on the front of the lathe bed and just beneath the ways. The rack enables the carriage to move along the ways either by hand or automatically.

CROSS-SLIDE

This is the casting fitted and mounted on the saddle and caused to move across the ways by means of a screwed spindle operated by a handwheel at the front of the saddle. The lathe tool is thus made to cut deeper, or may be made to cut right across the end of a piece of work.

It is usual to fix a graduated collar on the cross-slide handwheel so that a known movement can be transmitted to the cross-slide.

COMPOUND REST

This is the arrangement fitted to the cross slide. It consists of a SWIVEL SLIDE which acts like a turntable, and may be locked in any position by means of set screws or nuts. The purpose of moving it about is for the cutting of short tapers and the cross-slide block is marked off in degrees to enable accurate setting to be made from a datum mark on the swivel slide.

THE TOP SLIDE is fitted to the swivel slide and may be wound along its length from about 50 to 60 mm by means of a small handle at the right hand end.

A TOOL POST of some kind is mounted at the left hand of the top slide and this holds the lathe tool for cutting purposes. Tool posts are many and varied, the best being those that securely grip the tool as far to the left of the top slide as possible, so that machining can be carried out close up to the chuck jaws. This is most important when parting-off and knurling.

STRIPS

There are three main sliding parts to a lathe, 1. the SADDLE, 2. the CROSS SLIDE, and 3. the TOP SLIDE, and strips provide for the adjustment of wear on these surfaces so that the moving parts always fit correctly.

It is important to examine the setting of the strips of these moving parts before using a lathe. The sliding surfaces should be oiled or greased and the parts moved back and forth by hand before attempting to apply power feeds.

LATHE CENTRES, Fig. 151

These are two cone-shaped pieces of carbon steel accurately machined and tapered to fit, one in the headstock mandrel and the other in the tailstock quill. These tapers, known

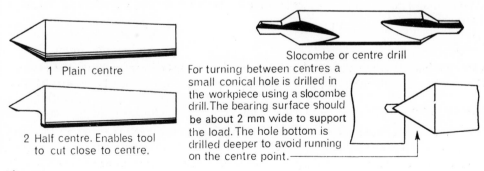

1 Plain centre

Slocombe or centre drill

2 Half centre. Enables tool to cut close to centre.

For turning between centres a small conical hole is drilled in the workpiece using a slocombe drill. The bearing surface should be about 2 mm wide to support the load. The hole bottom is drilled deeper to avoid running on the centre point.

Fig. 151

as MORSE TAPERS, provide a secure grip. The ends of the centres are ground to an inclusive angle of 60° and are used to support the ends of shafts, especially when turning between centres.

Because it rotates, that in the headstock end is known as the LIVE CENTRE and is usually left in the normalized state because it experiences no wear, furthermore it can be quickly and easily turned up true should it begin to run out of centre. To get the most accurate results, the side of this centre and the mandrel nose end should be marked in some way to ensure the same alignment every time the centre is used. The tailstock centre does not rotate and for this reason it is known as a DEAD CENTRE and must be hardened. In use it is actually a cone bearing upon which the work rotates, often at high speeds, and care must be taken to keep this part well lubricated.

Normally, plain centres as just described are used, but there are several variations of this important component according to the special needs of particular jobs.

LATHE SIZE, Fig. 152

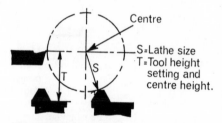

Fig. 152

The size of a lathe in Great Britain is known by the RADIUS of the largest piece of work which can be held in the chuck, and which will just clear the ways. Thus a 90 mm lathe will take a piece of work having a maximum diameter of 180 mm, assuming the work is being set up centrally, of course.

Sometimes the scope of a lathe may be increased by having a short length of the lathe bed removable at the chuck end so that extra large work can be accommodated, usually on the faceplate. Such lathes are known as gap bed lathes.

Lathe tools, Fig. 153

Lathe tools are generally made from carbon steel or high-speed steel (H.S.S.), the latter being by far the more popular even though expensive. Carbon steel has the advantage that it may be bought in long lengths, sawn off, forged, filed and ground to any desired shape or form, then hardened and tempered, thus giving the operator considerable scope in the design of his tool. Unfortunately carbon steel must be used with care because overheating will 'draw' the temper and render the tool soft and useless. Depth of cut must be light while the speed and feed should be slow enough to keep the tool cool. The use of a suitable coolant also helps to prevent overheating.

H.S.S. is used much more, being bought in short lengths of square section and known as tool bits. It is not possible to forge and form the end in the workshop so the tool shape is limited to grinding the front, side and top of the blank.

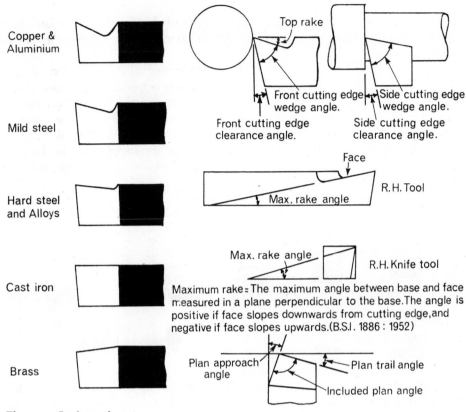

Copper &
Aluminium

Mild steel

Hard steel
and Alloys

Cast iron

Brass

Top rake

Front cutting edge
wedge angle.

Side cutting edge
wedge angle.

Front cutting edge
clearance angle.

Side cutting edge
clearance angle.

Face

Max. rake angle

R.H. Tool

Max. rake angle

R.H. Knife tool

Maximum rake = The maximum angle between base and face
measured in a plane perpendicular to the base. The angle is
positive if face slopes downwards from cutting edge, and
negative if face slopes upwards.(B.S.I. 1886 : 1952)

Plan approach
angle

Plan trail angle

Included plan angle

Fig. 153 Lathe tools

CUTTING ACTION

To enable the lathe tool to be fed into the work the front face must be ground away to an
angle of between 6° and 10°. This is called FRONT CLEARANCE and prevents the work
rubbing on the front of the tool. To enable the tool to cut along the work the side face of
the tool must be ground away to an angle of between 6° and 10°. This is called SIDE
CLEARANCE and prevents the work rubbing on the side of the tool.

The wedge action so necessary for cutting is achieved by grinding away the top of the
tool by an amount depending upon the material being cut. Thus for soft metals such as
copper and aluminium, the angle on the top should be between 25° and 35°, while for
ordinary steels an angle of 15° to 20° is desirable. Hard steels and ferrous alloys require a
slight angle, 10° being sufficient. The angle of metal ground away on the top of the tool
is known as the RAKE.

Cast iron being a metal which crumbles when cut instead of curling away as do the
steels, does not require any rake. Instead, the top is left quite flat, that is, the rake is zero.

Brass, as has been said before, is a peculiar metal to cut and any attempt to use a tool having normal rake will end in failure and probably disaster. The correct wedge form should be one in which the rake is negative, the angle being from about 2° to 5°. This type of tool will cut brass quickly and easily without any 'digging in' whatsoever.

As only a small length of the cutting edge should be in contact with the work, part of the front edge is ground back several degrees and this is known as the plan trail angle.

Lathe tools are known as RIGHT HAND, LEFT HAND or FRONT, and refer to that part of the work which they would cut, Fig. 154.

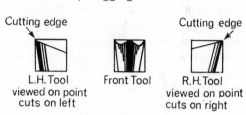

L.H. Tool viewed on point cuts on left   Front Tool   R.H. Tool viewed on point cuts on right

Fig. 154

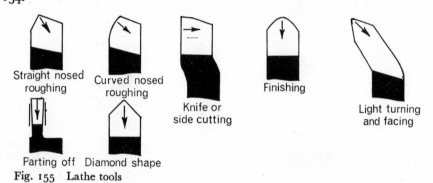

Straight nosed roughing   Curved nosed roughing   Knife or side cutting   Finishing   Light turning and facing

Parting off   Diamond shape

Fig. 155   Lathe tools

SOME CUTTING TOOLS, Fig. 155

ROUGHING TOOL

This is an excellent tool for removing a lot of waste metal quickly and easily, because it is capable of deep cuts.

KNIFE TOOL

This is useful for most work, especially when turning lengths of rod between centres, as the thrust is directed along the length of the work, thereby causing little tendency for it to bend.

This tool can be shaped to give a round nose or a square nose, the latter being necessary for working in corners.

FINISHING TOOL

This tool requires front rake only with a rounded nose, together with the usual front and side clearances. If the work has a large diameter and a short length, a broader nosed tool can be used than for finishing a small diameter piece of work of longer length. Speed and feed are also important, a slightly slower speed and a light cut helping to reduce the risk of vibration.

It must be added that a 'mirror finish' on steel is only obtainable in the last instance by the copious flow of cooling oil.

PARTING-OFF TOOL

This is another tool which demands great care in grinding and setting up in the lathe, which must be in good condition if parting-off is to be successful. The blade should be about 3 mm wide and about 20 mm long, but these sizes are merely given as a guide. The blade is off set to the left so that parting-off can be carried out as close to the jaws as possible. For clearance, the blade should taper about $\frac{1}{2}°$ from the cutting edge to the back on each side to prevent the tool sides jamming in the groove being cut. Both sides of the blade should also have 2° clearance from top to bottom and 6° front clearance. The rake should be 5° for steel, nil for cast iron and from 2° to 5° negative for brass.

Great care is required to set the tool so that the blade can cut right to the centre of the

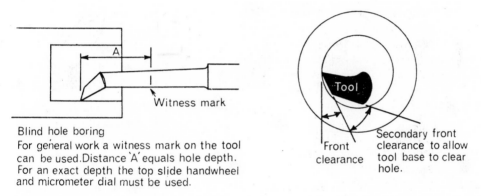

Blind hole boring
For general work a witness mark on the tool can be used. Distance 'A' equals hole depth. For an exact depth the top slide handwheel and micrometer dial must be used.

Front clearance   Secondary front clearance to allow tool base to clear hole.

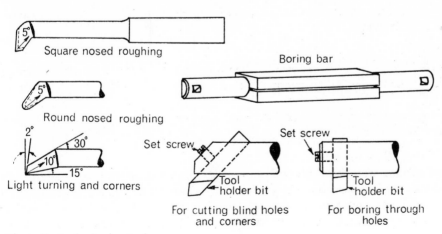

Fig. 156   Lathe boring tools

work without the blade sides interfering. Although the speed should be a little slower than normally required for cutting the material, it is possible to go too slow and cause the tool to labour. The strips require adjusting to remove all play and plenty of cooling oil must be applied when parting-off steel.

BORING TOOLS, Fig. 156

These may be purchased or made by forging a piece of carbon steel to shape, filing, grinding, and then hardening and tempering. The shaft must be as short as possible to avoid its bending in use. Front clearance is usually the problem here as the bottom of the tool may scrape in the hole being bored especially when opening out small holes. To overcome this, a second clearance is ground on the tool base to remove the corner.

TOOL BITS, Fig. 157

A useful method when plain turning is to use 3 mm and 6 mm square tool bits. These are short lengths of H.S.S. from 50 to 60 mm long. Owing to the high cost of the ordinary large tool bits and the fact that there is considerable wastage due to most of the shank being employed for hold-

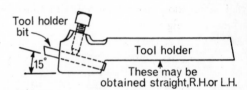

Fig. 157

ing purposes only, small tool bits are economical as well as being quickly and easily ground to shape. The bits are held in tool holders made of hardened alloy steel which in turn are clamped in the tool post. The slots for taking the bits slope at an angle of 15°, so that when assembled the cutter has already a front rake of 15° which is suitable for steel. Only the front and side clearances need to be ground, remembering to take into consideration the slope of the tool when secured in its holder. A further advantage is that the cutting edge is quickly set to the correct height because it can be moved up or down the slope, no packing being necessary.

KNURLING TOOL, Fig. 158

This tool is used for marking metal either with a diamond pattern or straight lines usually to facilitate hand holding such as on instrument screws, tap wrench handles and scribers. The diamond tool consists of a hardened alloy steel shank with a swivel-ling head containing two hardened wheels mounted one above the other and free to rotate. The shank must be set in the tool post so that when the two wheels are just mak-

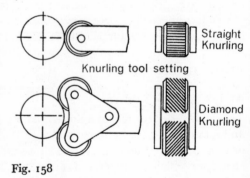

Fig. 158

ing contact with the work the two wheels are vertically in line. For a diamond pattern the helical grooves in each wheel are cut in opposite directions. The speed should be reduced by half and a little cooling oil used.

If the knurling has to be done along the length of bar, then the tool may be fed along the work to produce the desired effect.

Knurling tools are obtainable having large rotating heads containing three sets of wheels to give fine, medium or coarse diamond knurling. When straight knurling is required, a shank containing one wheel mounted centrally in the end must be used. The grooves in the wheel are, of course, cut straight across the wheel face. The tool must be mounted with the wheel centre to the normal tool height, so that the tool and work oppose each other in a horizontal plane. The operation is continued until the grooves on the work match the grooves on the wheel of the tool.

SETTING UP TOOLS, Fig. 159

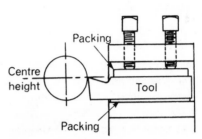

Fig. 159   Tool height

All lathe tools must be set in the tool post so that the height of their cutting edge is at the same height as the points of the lathe centres are above the ways. When facing off the end of a piece of metal this can easily be verified as, when the centre of the work is reached, a 'pimple' of metal will result if the tool is too high or too low.

If the tool is turning a length of metal, too high a setting will cause the work to rub on the tool rather than cut, while too low a setting will result in a scraping action rather than one of cutting because the angles of rake and clearance have been made false.

More often than not the cutting edge is just below the required height when first placed in the tool post, and the tool must be packed up with strips of tinplate and steel. These packing strips should be neatly cut to the size of the tool, and where possible one or two thick strips ought to be used in preference to many thin pieces of packing.

It is also advisable to use a strip of steel about 3 mm thick at least on top of the tool to distribute evenly the pressure from the holding down screws and avoid tool breakage.

TOOL HOLDERS

AMERICAN TYPE

This tool holder consists of a slotted bar located in a T-slot in the top slide, free to move and rotate when setting up the tool. The tool is packed up to the correct centre height as near as possible, final adjustment being made by tilting the boat upon which the tool rests after which the holding down bolt or screw is tightened up.

This may seem an ingenious idea at first glance, as exact tool setting is quickly obtained without the bother of trial and error with various strips of packing, but the tool post is not recommended, because the tilting of the tool destroys the effect of the rake and clearance angles.

FOUR-WAY TOOL POST

This consists of a square steel block clamped through the centre to the top slide, and having a groove cut all round the four edges enabling four tools to be mounted at once. The turret can then be easily rotated to bring any one of the four tools in place, a ratchet stop ensuring that the tool post always stops in the same position. This type of tool holder offers maximum support to the tool with extreme left side location.

Although four tools are not always required in the tool post at the same time, the 'set up' is useful when carrying out repetition work using the knurling and parting-off tools among others.

THE BACK GEAR

The back gear is a device used to reduce the speed of rotation of the work in the lathe.

To use the back gear, the bull wheel must first be disconnected from the speed cones, then the back gears are brought into mesh with the headstock gears by means of some lever arrangement. The drive from the belt now causes the cone and its pinion to rotate, driving the gear wheel and pinion of the back gear which drives the bull wheel keyed to the mandrel.

These slow speeds are desirable when turning large work, hard metals, knurling, parting-off and screwcutting. To resume normal speed, the back gear is first disengaged, then the bull wheel locked to the cones. It need hardly be said that the lathe must always be stopped before attempting any changes in speeds or gearing.

TUMBLER GEARS

This is a device for reversing the rotation of the lead screw and feed shaft.

It consists of three gear wheels in mesh and mounted on a swivelling plate or tumbler which is free to rotate about the stud wheel.

CHUCKS

THREE-JAW CHUCK AND BACK-PLATE, Fig. 160

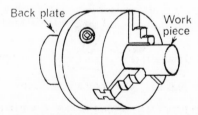

Fig. 160   Three jaw chuck

This chuck is sometimes called the self-centring chuck because the jaws all move together when the chuck key is turned. Only truly cylindrical or hexagonal work should be held in it, otherwise the jaws will be severely strained and cease to run true.

It is advisable to use all three positions round the chuck for tightening purposes so as to distribute the strain on the scroll. The gripping power is not high and only small or light work should be employed in this chuck. The jaws are stepped and shaped to offer versatility when in use, work being held both inside or on the outside of any of the steps provided according to its diameter.

The chuck is bolted to a cast iron back plate, which is bored and screwed to fasten on the nose of the mandrel. A landing strip is machined on the two parts so that the chuck can be mounted squarely on the mandrel before screwing on begins, and thus save misalignment and damage to the thread.

FOUR-JAW CHUCK AND BACK-PLATE, Fig. 161

This is a larger and more robust chuck than the three-jaw type. Four independently operated jaws are provided, stepped, grooved and shaped to give maximum versatility of the work it can take. The chuck face has a series of concentric rings machined on it, which greatly helps the setting of the jaws prior to inserting the work. The holding power of this chuck is strong, mainly because of the thread used for tightening purposes.

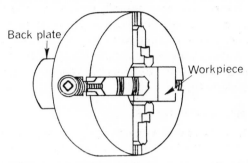

Fig. 161   Four jaw chuck

By reversing one or more jaws, a wide variety of irregular shaped work can be mounted and securely held for turning. This chuck is also bolted to a backplate which is bored and screwed to fasten on the mandrel nose.

When using the three- and four-jaw chucks, see that the ends of the jaws do not project beyond the rim of the chuck. Apart from being dangerous to the operator, it indicates that the work is too big for the chuck.

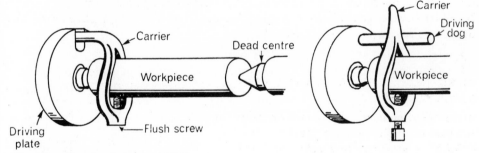

Fig. 162   Turning between centres

DRIVING PLATE OR CATCH PLATE, Fig. 162

A small-diameter faceplate made in one piece and bored and screwed to fit on the mandrel nose. One or two slots are machined in the face to take a steel pin called a 'DRIVING DOG', its purpose being to push the CARRIER secured to the work mounted between centres and so cause rotation. There is some danger to the operator here due to the tail of the carrier projecting outwards from the work, and also the length of the driving dog.

A better method is to use carriers having a long tail bent over at right angles which lie in a slot in the driving plate. Carriers are obtainable in different sizes to fit a variety of different sized shafts. Work which must not be marked by the carrier should have a strip of brass of copper wound round it.

FACEPLATE

This is a much larger diameter faceplate than the catch plate, but is also made in one piece, bored and screwed to fit on the mandrel nose. It has slots and square holes right through the face so that bolts can be used to clamp work to its face. Much ingenuity is often needed when setting up work on the faceplate. Very often, packing strips must be used to mount the work off the faceplate so that the tool can clear the work. Holding clamps may have to be specially made, together with packing blocks, or an angle plate may have to be bolted to the faceplate first, and the work bolted or clamped to it, using V blocks, clamps and packing strips.

Quite often, especially when the angle plate is used, the faceplate is out of balance and this must be corrected by bolting weights to counterbalance this. Gear wheels are useful for this work and the faceplate must be tried by hand rotation to ensure as smooth a movement as possible before engaging power drive. Even then, very slow speeds are essential.

GENERAL

When removing a chuck, put the lathe in low gear and place a block of hardwood, not quite as high as the centre height, on the lathe ways farthest from the operator. Reverse the rotation by jerking on the motor belt so that the chuck jaw bounces against the end of the hardwood block, when it should loosen. Place the left hand well under the chuck and the right hand on top and carefully unscrew it until it is off the thread. It helps if a block of wood is made to fit over the ways for protection beneath the chuck in case of accidental dropping and damaging of the ways.

When fitting a chuck, see that the mandrel thread and the chuck thread are perfectly clean and free from particles of metal and grit. For this reason, the chucks not in use should be covered in some way and not left in the open to collect workshop scrap until wanted. If in doubt, clean the backplate thread and bore with a brush dipped in paraffin, then clean dry with a non-fluffy cloth. Smear lightly with oil and assemble, first by placing the chuck on the spindle, then gently engaging the threads.

Failure to clean out these mating parts may cause the chuck to run out of truth and create difficulty later on when attempting to remove it. Finally, always run the lathe to see that the newly assembled chuck is running true.

15

Setting up Work for Turning

For round bar less than 25 mm in diameter the three-jaw chuck is satisfactory, but for sizes above this, and, of course, square or rectangular bar, the four-jaw chuck must be used. Its gripping power is greater and the work can be set accurately, for one seldom finds a self-centring chuck running true.

When rough castings have to be turned, the jaws should be opened to the approximate size, using a rule and the concentric rings on the chuck face as a guide. As there is no true face or datum line on a casting, accurate setting does not arise and it is enough to present a piece of chalk to the fast-revolving work to mark it, Fig. 163. The jaws should be adjusted to get an even scattering of chalk marks all round by slackening back one jaw and tightening the opposite, finally tightening the first. This should be repeated on the other pair of jaws if necessary.

If accurately machined work has to be set up, the work is first measured across the part to be held, and the jaws opened out so as just to receive it, then lightly tightened up. A surface gauge must now be used adjusting opposite pairs of jaws, Fig. 164.

When turning between centres, first check from the drawing whether the centres are to remain in the finished work or not. If they are to remain, then the stock need only be sawn off about 2 mm longer to allow for lightly facing off the ends. If the work is to be finished without the centres showing, then the stock must be sawn off about 14 mm longer to allow for facing off upon completion of the work. The ends of the workpiece are then faced off in the chuck and centre holes drilled using a centre or slocombe drill. Before mounting the work between centres, check that they are in line by bringing them

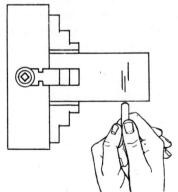

Fig. 163   Approximate setting

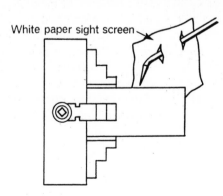

White paper sight screen

Fig. 164   Accurate setting

together, adjusting the tailstock if necessary, Fig. 165. Having fixed the carrier on the work, the tailstock centre should be rubbed with a little tallow, oil or grease, and the centre adjusted by means of the tailstock handwheel so that the work revolves freely but without end play. It may be necessary to turn the compound rest round 10° or so because the top slide will probably foul the tailstock and prevent the tool being fed in to the work. Only a minimum length of the tailstock barrel should project, and the clamping lever should be used to remove 'play'.

Before attempting any lathe work, the carriage should be wound along by hand while rotating the driving plate, also by hand, to see how far along the work the cut may go without catching any moving parts. A chalk mark should be made on the work and cutting kept within this limit for safety.

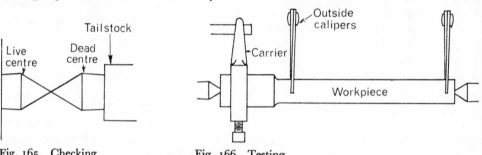

Fig. 165   Checking   Fig. 166   Testing

When turning begins, only a light cut should be made at first, the idea being to test the work to see whether it is being cut parallel or not. This is checked by trying both ends of the cut with outside calipers, Fig. 166. If both parts are the same size, then the work is parallel and the work may proceed, but this is seldom the case. If the work is larger at the tailstock end, this part must be moved over towards the operator, and this is done by winding the carriage along to bring the tool to rest within, say, 1 mm from the work. A piece of white paper placed on the cross-slide beneath the tool helps the operator to·see the gap between work and tool more clearly. The tailstock clamping lever is then slightly released and the screws adjusted to move the work until it touches the tool, Fig. 167.

Having made the adjustment, and tightened both screws, lock the tailstock clamping lever and tighten up the tailstock centre which will have moved since the pressure was released. Now take off a light cut right along the work as far as possible and once again check to see if the work is parallel.

If the tailstock end is turning smaller, then the tool is brought up to just touch the work at the

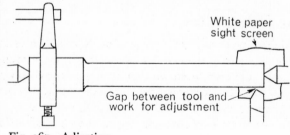

Fig. 167   Adjusting

144

tailstock end. Slight adjustment is then made to the loosehead, but this time the work is moved away from the tool to leave a small gap. This trial-and-error method must be continued until the lathe is cutting parallel.

After several cuts have been made along the work, the metal becomes warm and expands, so that a constant check must be made of the pressure on the centres.

TURNING TAPERS

There are three ways in which a taper can be turned in a lathe: 1. using the compound slide, 2. offsetting the tailstock, 3. using a taper-turning attachment.

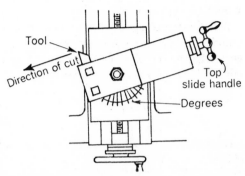

Fig. 168   Taper turning

The compound slide method consists of slackening two nuts or screws and rotating the swivel block to the required angle as shown by the scale of degrees on the cross-slide block and the witness mark on the swivel. The taper can only be turned by using the top slide, and the taper length is limited to the travel which seldom exceeds 50 mm. Both internal and external tapers can be turned and because of the short, large angles possible, they are referred to as 'quick' tapers, Fig. 168.

The tailstock offset method simply means moving the tailstock out of line with the main axis of the lathe so that the work is not cut parallel. Only external tapers are possible by this method and the angles are small, consequently they are known as 'slow' tapers. The ordinary pointed lathe centres are not suitable for this kind of taper turning because they fail to line up with the axis of the holes drilled in the ends of the work, in fact on large tapers the centres become damaged. Much better results are to be had by using ball ended centres.

A still more satisfactory method is to use a taper turning attachment. This has the advantage in that holes can be tapered as well as the outsides, also when turning between centres the two centres must be in line with the main axis so that no distortion occurs at these points.

SURFACING CUTS

Machining the end of a piece of metal is known as SURFACING and care must be taken if the diameter of the work is large, otherwise the result will not be as flat as it should be. Some lathes are fitted with an arrangement whereby the cross-slide can be made to self act across the work, giving a clean even surface. However, the resistance of the lathe tool to cutting causes the carriage slowly to move away, resulting in a convex face. This can be overcome by tightening up on the carriage strips to secure it to the ways, or the tailstock can be brought up against the carriage to hold it.

145

In any case, it is as well to take a light cut over to finish off the work and always test with a rule before removing the work from the lathe.

Where the lathe is not fitted with an automatic surfacing feed the tool must be fed across by hand. Tedious though this may be, it has the advantage that the carriage can be positively secured to the bed by engaging the lead screw lever with the lead screw shaft in neutral. Care must be taken after engaging this lever that all backlash is removed by winding the carriage as far towards the tailstock end as it will go.

When turning by hand, make the wheel causing the tool to move over the work revolve as evenly as possible. This is done by using two hands, one above and one below the wheel, one hand slowly rotating the wheel while the other hand returns to take over.

When using the feed on SLIDING cuts, that is, parallel to the lathe ways, and especially when working up to shoulders, the feed lever must be disengaged promptly. Never let it go to the end of the cut, for not only does this gradually shorten the shoulder at the best, but the shock to the tool may break it.

MANDRELS

Occasionally it happens that a small component has to be turned all over on the outside to some particular shape which must be quite true to its bore. Such a component cannot, of course, be held in a chuck. Instead it is assembled on a shaft which is then mounted between centres where the outside of the work can be freely turned. Such a shaft is called a MANDREL and to hold the work securely it is turned with a taper in the region of 0.1 mm per 120 mm, Fig. 169.

After boring out the work to size, it is driven on the shaft by means of a mallet or press to obtain a good fit and avoid damaging the mandrel centres. A carrier must be secured to the shaft, which is then mounted between centres. It is usual for the smaller end of the mandrel to be positioned at the tailstock end so that normal turning to the left does not tend to loosen the work from its mounting.

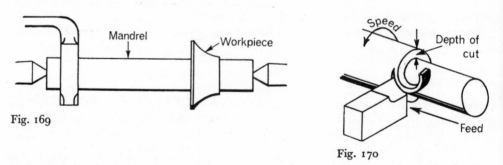

Fig. 169

Fig. 170

Lathe speeds and feeds

When turning, three important details must be considered for the successful removal of waste metal:

1. The depth of cut, which is the distance the tool penetrates beneath the surface of the work.

2. The feed, or the rate at which the cut is moving across the work.

3. The speed, which is the revolutions per minute of the mandrel and consequently the work, Fig. 170.

The depth of cut varies with the size and shape of the work, the material of which it is made, and the manner in which it is held. For the roughing down of ordinary mild steel, the feed should be about 0.25 mm per revolution, while for brass 0.5 mm is better, but when light finishing cuts are applied, the feeds should be slowed down to about 0.15 and 0.2 mm respectively.

Tables are available showing the recommended cutting speeds in millimetres per minute for various common metals and alloys using H.S.S. tools, and from these tables the operator can easily calculate the speed at which to run his lathe from the formula:

$$\text{Revs. per minute of mandrel} = \frac{\text{Cutting speed in mm per min.}}{\text{Circumference of work in mm}}$$

For roughing out mild steel a cutting speed of 24000 mm per minute is satisfactory using a H.S.S. tool. The correct speed for turning a 25 mm bar of mild steel would therefore be:

$$\text{Revs. per minute of mandrel} = \frac{\text{Cutting speed in mm per min.}}{\text{Circumference of work in mm}}$$

$$\frac{24000}{25 \times 3.14}$$

$$= 305$$

If the formula results in a speed not available on the lathe, select the nearest speed below that required, remembering that if a lot of metal has to be removed, the speed can be increased later as the diameter of the work decreases.

In general, light finishing cuts should have higher speeds and finer feeds than roughing cuts.

CHATTERING

Occasionally when turning, a rippled pattern develops along the surface of the workpiece, accompanied by a burring noise which can be alarming. This is called 'chatter' and is caused by vibration. In almost every case a reduced speed will eliminate the trouble though it may be necessary at first to drop to a lower than normal speed to remove the chatter marks. It is also necessary to check over the lathe 'set up'. Is the workpiece properly held and supported? If the tailstock is in use, is it making contact with the work? Is the tool adequately held in the tool post with minimum overhang?

A common cause of chatter is too long a cutting edge in contact with the workpiece.

It may be necessary to regrind the tool to reduce this, but quite often it is sufficient to move the tool round a few degrees to present a narrower cutting edge. Having examined the tool angles and the setting, it is as well to check that the cutting edge is set to the correct height. Finally, the strips may require adjusting.

If chatter still persists, it could be that the headstock mandrel bearings are worn, in which case the remedy, though costly and time consuming, is the fitting of new ones.

Chattering can occur on all machines, and quite often the remedy is simply to reduce the speed. This is particularly so when using the drilling machine.

One should guard against expecting work to be correct because a setting has been made to a witness mark. It will, no doubt, be very close, but unless the operator has been very lucky he will have to make several trial-and-error adjustments as the work proceeds, using a gauge of some sort constantly to check the accuracy.

BACKLASH

Backlash may be defined as the amount of movement in a wheel, spindle or gear when its direction is reversed and it causes no movement to its mating part. If these parts were fitted so that there was no backlash they would be too stiff to move.

16

Foundrywork

The art of casting is probably five thousand years old. For much of this time stone or baked clay moulds were used, moulding boxes being introduced in the later Middle Ages. The skill with which these early races handled molten metal can be judged from the intricate castings made for various parts of Solomon's Temple built at Jerusalem and described in 1 Kings 7 : 23, 25, 26, 46, and 2 Chronicles 4 : 2, 4, 5, 17.

Moulding is the art of shaping metal by melting and pouring it into a prepared hollow. This enables complicated shapes to be quickly and simply made as compared with the alternative method of either machining from the solid, or fitting and building up in sections.

THE PATTERN

The purpose of the pattern is to produce the hollow in the moulding sand into which molten metal will be poured. It should be made from some easily worked material such as wood, though plaster and metal are also used in industry. Clean, straight-grained timber which has been well seasoned is essential, yellow pine, white pine and mahogany being best. Woods that tend to warp and twist should be avoided. Simple patterns may be turned on the lathe or chiselled and sawn to shape, while complicated patterns are more easily made by building up in pieces and using waterproof glue.

The important part of the casting should be arranged to lie face downwards in the mould, partly because the dross from the molten metal rises, and partly because the weight of metal above assists in ensuring better detail in the lowest part of the casting.

To enable the pattern to leave the mould cleanly and without scraping the sides all vertical faces should taper about 3 to 5 degrees and this is called TAPER or DRAW, Fig. 171. Owing to the contraction of the molten metal on cooling in the mould, the pattern should be made a little bigger to allow for this and special contraction rules are available to avoid tedious calculation of every dimension. If part of the casting has to be machined, a machining allowance has to be made on that surface, and for most work, 3 mm is enough.

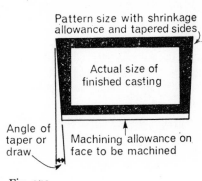

Pattern size with shrinkage allowance and tapered sides

Actual size of finished casting

Angle of taper or draw

Machining allowance on face to be machined

Fig. 171

149

Finally, some consideration must be given to the method of holding the casting while it is being machined, because it may be necessary to provide lugs or bosses for locating it in the chuck or clamping it to the faceplate, such appendages being machined off in the final stages of the work. Simple patterns can be made in one piece, such as those having one face completely flat, but most patterns have to be made in two pieces for the purpose of removing the pattern after making each half of the mould in separate boxes, which are then clamped together.

Some thought must be given as to where the 'parting line' should be. First, it must be decided which way the pattern will lie in the sand so that it can be withdrawn easily, and from this, the parting line can be found being usually the greatest perimeter of the object. The two halves of the pattern should be dowelled to give accurate location, the dowels being tapered to ensure instant separation of the two parts, Fig. 172. The surface of the patterns must be finished

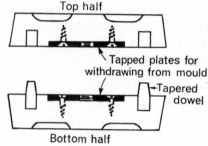

Fig. 172   Split pattern

quite smooth with all internal corners rounded off by means of leather strips glued in place, or filled in with plastic wood pressed to shape using a pencil. The pattern is then given two coats of varnish to prevent sand 'pick up' from the mould and moisture absorption which would cause warping.

Pattern parts are generally painted different colours to indicate their importance or purpose to the moulder, so that he can plan his work better. The British Standards recommendation for colouring patterns is:

1.   Red or orange to denote casting parts to be left in the cast state.
2.   Yellow to denote casting parts which have to be machined.
3.   Black for core prints.

MOULDING SAND

Moulding sand consists of grains of sand coated with clay. The sand ensures porosity which is essential for the escape of the steam and gas generated in the mould when the molten metal pours in, while the clay binds the sand together to give smoothness and cohesion. The sand should be thoroughly raked and mixed with water to bring it to the correct 'temper'. That is, it should be moist enough to hold together when grasped firmly, but loose enough to break easily when thrown back on the moulding bench.

Dampness must be avoided at all costs when moulding, as spattering and explosions will result if molten metal comes in contact with it. For this reason all tools must be well heated before use, and moulds must be warmed just before pouring the metal.

Moulds may be either, 'greensand', or 'dry-sand'. For greensand moulds, materials must be added to the sand to separate the grains and make them less liable to fuse together when washed by the molten metal. The 'open' texture of the sand also allows the gases to escape more easily when casting takes place. Coal dust is one of the commonest substances added, but it must be realized that the cohesive quality of the sand is slightly reduced, and the mixture should never contain more than 8 per cent coal dust.

The term greensand simply means that the mould is left in its moist state and has no reference to the colour of the sand, which may vary from red to black. Only greensand moulding is considered here.

Dry sand moulds refer to moulds which are carefully dried in an oven before use. The sand used for this type of work must be of a heavier nature with more clay, so as to retain its shape when dried out, ordinary greensand mixtures being unsuitable because they would crumble after baking.

PARTING POWDER

A dry powder unaffected by moisture and dusted over the moulding sand to ensure smooth separation of the flasks. Burnt sand, bone dust, powdered bath brick and various commercial preparations are used.

FLASKS, Fig. 173

Two flasks are normally used when making a mould, the top flask being called the COPE and the bottom one the DRAG. They must be strong enough to remain quite rigid. Cast iron is obviously the favourite metal though aluminium and steel are used as well.

The important points are that the cope and drag should register correctly by means of dowel pins located on the outsides, that there should be some means of securing the two flasks together to prevent the cope floating off when the mould is being filled with molten metal, and that a lip is provided around the inside edge to key the sand in each flask.

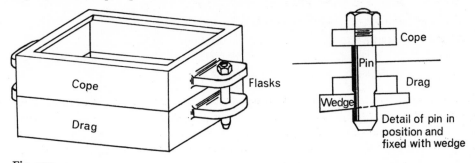

Fig. 173

CRUCIBLES, Fig. 174

Crucibles are the pots used for melting the metal which is to be cast. They are made of plumbago, which is a mixture of graphite obtained from Madagascar and clays mainly from Dorset, finished off with a glaze which is burnt on. Glazing is necessary to prevent the burning out of the graphite in the pots. Crucibles should be handled with the same

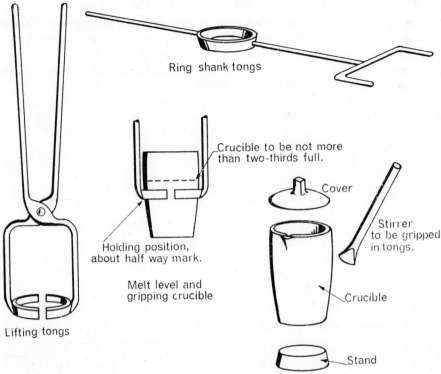

Ring shank tongs

Crucible to be not more than two-thirds full.

Cover

Stirrer to be gripped in tongs.

Holding position, about half way mark.

Melt level and gripping crucible

Crucible

Lifting tongs

Stand

Fig. 174

care as when handling crockery. The weakest part is the rim, and they should never be gripped at this part.

When charging the crucible, the pieces of metal should be clean and hot, it is dangerous to introduce cold metal as the extremes of temperature may cause spattering. A handy way is to stand lumps of metal round the furnace edge, or warm them up over the forge fire.

The metal pieces should be small enough to go right in the crucible without any risk of wedging on the sides, otherwise the expanding metal may crack the crucible. When completely charged, the crucible should be no more than about two-thirds full. It is advisable to stand the crucible on a plumbago base in the furnace and use a plumbago lid to prevent the melt from oxidizing as much as possible. After pouring the metal in the mould, any molten metal remaining should be poured into a prepared trough in the sand. If this is not done, when heated up next time, this metal will expand and break the crucible.

While still warm, it should be raked out to remove the slag which ought to come out as a thin shell, leaving the crucible clean and ready for storing away, though they last longer if used regularly.

152

MAKING A ONE-PIECE PATTERN MOULD, Fig. 175

To ensure smooth even faces on the mould and to facilitate the turning over of the flasks, two 'turning-over' boards are required. These can quite easily be made from 13 mm plywood a little bigger than the flasks and with two battens on one side to enable fingers to get beneath for holding purposes. The boards should be painted to prevent sand and moisture pick up.

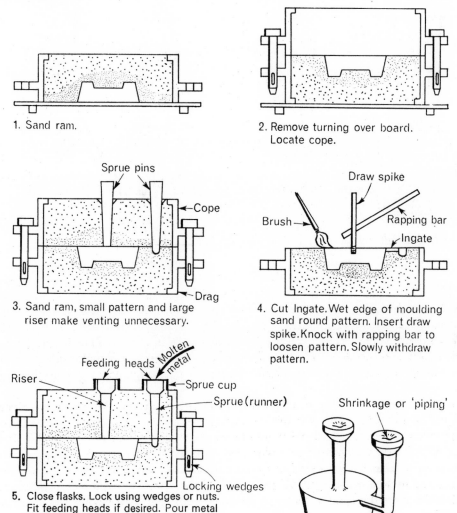

1. Sand ram.

2. Remove turning over board. Locate cope.

3. Sand ram, small pattern and large riser make venting unnecessary.

Sprue pins — Cope — Drag

4. Cut Ingate. Wet edge of moulding sand round pattern. Insert draw spike. Knock with rapping bar to loosen pattern. Slowly withdraw pattern.

Draw spike — Brush — Rapping bar — Ingate

Feeding heads — Molten metal — Riser — Sprue cup — Sprue (runner) — Locking wedges

5. Close flasks. Lock using wedges or nuts. Fit feeding heads if desired. Pour metal in steady stream until riser and sprue are both full.

Shrinkage or 'piping'

Appearance of casting after removal from mould

Fig. 175   Moulding and casting

F

To make a mould using two flasks and a one piece pattern, proceed as follows:

1. Place one turning-over board on the bench.

2. Place the drag upside down on the board.

3. Locate the pattern on the board, and position it so that there is at least 25 mm clear all round between it and the drag. It may be advisable to place it a little to one side to allow for the metal inlet.

4. Riddle sand over the pattern to a depth of 25 mm at least and peg ram carefully, using the fingers or a short length of 10 mm dowel'rod. It is essential to get the sand in close contact all over the pattern.

5. Unsifted sand is shovelled in and butt-rammed fairly hard until the flask is slightly more than full.

6. A thick steel straightedge is placed across the flask and the surplus sand removed by 'sawing' it off. This is called 'strickling off'.

7. If desired, a piece of 3 mm diameter brass wire can be used and holes prodded in the sand to within 12 mm of the casting for the purpose of venting the mould.

8. The second turning-over board is placed on top of the drag, and the whole unit of two boards and the flask turned completely over so that the bottom board is now on top.

9. Remove the top board and fit the cope on the drag. Take up any loose play by twisting the cope in a clockwise direction.

10. Two slightly tapered wooden pegs called sprue pins are now located. One is pressed about 20 mm down in the sand not more than 38 mm from the edge of the pattern. This sprue pin will make a vertical hole in the finished mould, known as the 'sprue', 'downgate' or 'runner'. The other sprue pin can be placed on the pattern and will enable gases and excess metal to flow up the hole to provide a 'head' of metal. This hole is called the 'riser'. The sprue pin should be rubbed smooth and varnished the same as the pattern.

11. A light dusting of parting powder from a linen bag is given to the surface of the sand in the drag to ensure clean separation of the two flasks later.

12. Again, sand is riddled to a depth of 25 mm and peg-rammed.

13. Sand is shovelled in and butt-rammed. This is a little more difficult owing to the two sprue pins projecting above the surface.

14. The sand is strickled off to level the top.

15. A pouring basin is cut around the gate sprue pin to enable a basin of metal to keep the runner full while the metal is being poured.

16. The sprue pins are tapped or worked sideways slightly to ease them in the sand, after which they are removed.

17. The pouring basin is trimmed up and a cylinder of metal is placed around the

basin to consolidate the sand there.

18. The cope is vented if necessary with the 3 mm diameter brass wire to within 12 mm of the pattern.

19. The cope is removed and carefully stood on one side.

20. The ingate is cut from the sprue hole in the drag. The depression here is called a skim bob because it helps to trap slag. The cross-sectional area of the ingate should be less than that of the downgate to check the rush of metal from the downgate. Slag will then be kept in the downgate and the mould will have a steady supply of metal pouring into it.

21. Using a soft brush, the sand is moistened all round the pattern edge.

22. A withdrawing spike is screwed into the pattern and rapped several times in different directions so as to loosen the pattern in the mould then withdrawn vertically using the right hand spread out to steady the pattern.

23. The cutting of the ingate is now completed by cutting from the mould end out-wards.

24. Minor repairs are made if necessary, remembering that it is better to have too little sand than too much. Too little means extra metal on the casting.

25. The mould is blown clean, using hand bellows.

26. The mould surface is dried and warmed to remove local dampness. Use a blow torch flame, or better still apply a proprietary dressing to the mould surface which is then set on fire. This not only warms the mould but gives the casting surface a better finish.

27. The drag is placed on a level surface consisting of several iron bars on a sandy floor. This enables venting of the drag to take place beneath.

28. The mould is closed by replacing the cope after a final blow with the bellows. Again a slight clockwise twist should be given to ensure exact location between cope and drag. The flasks must now be secured together by bolts, or tapered wedges, or a heavy weight could be placed across the top. This last method has the added advantage of preventing the sand from rising due to the pressure of the molten metal.

29. The metal, correctly heated and treated, is poured in a constant stream down the runner. When the runner and riser basins are both full, pouring ceases. As the metal cools and shrinks the casting is able to draw on the molten metal in the runner and riser until solidification sets in. After half an hour, when casting in aluminium, the flasks can be separated and the sand knocked out, but it may be another hour before the casting is cool enough to handle.

All that remains to be done now is to saw and chisel off the riser and runner connections, a process known as fettling. It is important when making up a mould to consider the problem of fettling when locating the sprue pins to ensure that fettling is possible.

MAKING A MOULD USING A SPLIT PATTERN

The procedure is exactly the same as for the one-piece pattern. The important half of the pattern is placed on the board and within the drag, which is upside down. Ram up the drag and turn over exactly as before, the other half of the pattern being then united to complete the whole object, tapered dowels ensuring accurate location.

MAKING AN ODDSIDE MOULD, Fig. 176

It may be necessary to make a mould from a pattern which is in one piece but will not lie on the turnover board so that its parting line comes level with the face of the flask, a simple example being the casting of a sphere. In this case a box of some sort must be used to support the pattern—a flask will do for convenience, and the cope is generally used.

The cope is filled with sand and the pattern pressed in and adjusted until its parting line is level with the surface of the sand in which it rests. This support is called an ODDSIDE and this method of making a mould known as oddside moulding. Where many moulds have to be made from the same pattern it is economical in both time and labour to make an oddside out of plaster of Paris. Oddside moulding is a convenient way of using a pattern which has a difficult parting line, and thereby saves the labour of awkward joint making.

Having supported the bottom part of the pattern which lies below the parting line, the drag is placed upside down over the top and the mould prepared exactly as before when beginning. It will be necessary to use parting sand to ensure a clean separation between the drag and the oddside.

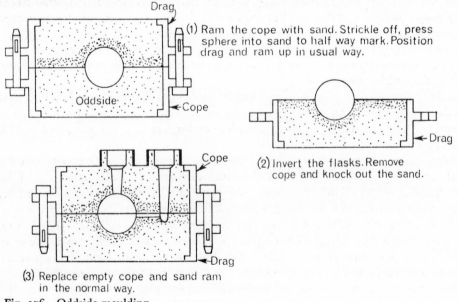

(1) Ram the cope with sand. Strickle off, press sphere into sand to half way mark. Position drag and ram up in usual way.

(2) Invert the flasks. Remove cope and knock out the sand.

(3) Replace empty cope and sand ram in the normal way.

Fig. 176   Oddside moulding

When the drag has been correctly filled with sand, the whole unit is turned over, the oddside is removed, exposing the pattern lying partly in the drag and partly above. The empty cope is correctly positioned on the drag, the sprue pins are located, parting sand dusted over and the flask filled as before.

CORE MAKING, Fig. 177

If a casting has to be made with a hole in it, a shaped piece of sand must be placed in position to prevent the molten metal filling up that space. The shaped piece of sand is called a CORE, and has to be specially prepared. There are several different ways of making cores using various ingredients depending upon the size and intricacy of the casting as well as the metal being cast, but a simple and general method is to mix silica sand with a little water and linseed oil. The linseed oil acts as a binding agent in the finished core, and the water supplies a little body to the sand while it is in its green state.

To mould the core to the desired shape means that a core box must be made. This should consist of two halves of wood dowelled together to give correct location, and the inside bored or carved to the required shape. It may be necessary to provide a vent hole right through the core and this is done by placing a piece of 3 mm diameter wire in the box as the core is made. If the core is curved, then a piece of waxed string must be used instead, so as to facilitate removal after baking. It may also be necessary to reinforce the core by inserting one or two wires in the core sand.

Having rammed the prepared sand in the core box together with the venting wire and reinforcing rods, the box is opened and the core carefully removed. It is now baked slowly until it is hard and dry, at a temperature of 200°C. It is important not to exceed this temperature, otherwise it weakens the bond.

To enable the core to be placed in position in the mould, the pattern has to be made with projections known as CORE PRINTS, which leave recesses in the sand into which the core just fits without moving.

For small light work, a greensand core can be used, but requires care in handling as it lacks the strength of a baked core. In some cases steel is used, giving a fine hard finish to the casting. Intricate shapes are best made by bonding separate cores together with a special core bond.

Compressed-air spray guns enable various liquid preparations to be sprayed on the mould surface to assist the production of a clean casting. In many instances it will be found that the ordinary 'Flit' type of spray will give quite satisfactory results. The riddle, or sieve, should have 3 mm mesh to ensure that no foreign matter finds its way into the sand in the immediate vicinity of the pattern. Sprue sticks need to be about 150 mm long and turned with a taper being about 50 mm diameter at the top and 25 mm diameter at the bottom for aluminium casting, while 30 mm diameter at the top and 25 mm diameter at the bottom is sufficient for cast-iron work. The drawspike consists of a length of 6 mm diameter steel rod screwed at one end to engage a tapped plate let into the pattern, and the rapping bar is simply a short length of 12 mm steel bar, Fig. 178.

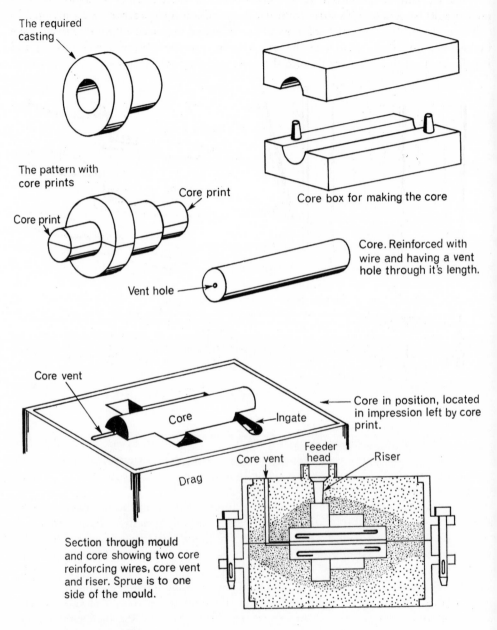

The required casting

The pattern with core prints

Core print

Core print

Vent hole

Core box for making the core

Core. Reinforced with wire and having a vent hole through it's length.

Core vent

Core

Ingate

Core in position, located in impression left by core print.

Feeder head

Riser

Core vent

Drag

Section through mould and core showing two core reinforcing wires, core vent and riser. Sprue is to one side of the mould.

Fig. 177   Core moulding

When working in aluminium all iron and steel tools which have to be immersed in the melt should be coated with some proprietary preparation to prevent 'iron pick up'.

The tools are dipped in this solution and well heated before attempting to place them in the melt. It is advisable to have the tools at or near red heat beforehand for safety, and it helps to have the forge fire lit with the tools warming ready for use.

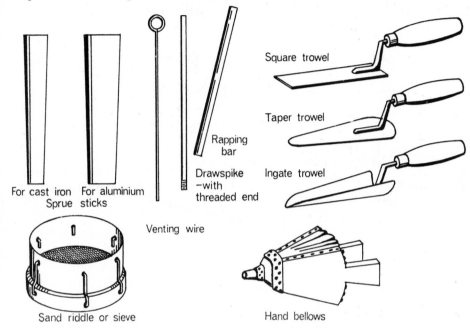

For cast iron   For aluminium
    Sprue sticks

Rapping bar

Drawspike
—with
threaded end

Square trowel

Taper trowel

Ingate trowel

Venting wire

Sand riddle or sieve

Hand bellows

Fig. 178

17

Bolts, Set Screws and Spanners

BOLTS, Fig. 179

These enable components to be fastened together by tightening a nut on the screwed end
Bolt heads are normally hexagonal, particularly for engineering use, but they may also be square, cup, countersunk, cheese, or in fact any shape convenient to the work in hand.

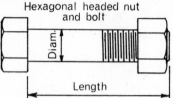

Hexagonal headed nut and bolt

Diam.

Length

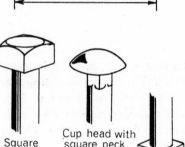

Square head

Cup head with square neck

'T-head for use on machine tables

Wing or butterfly nut

Square nut

Fig. 179   Bolts

STUDS, Fig. 180

In many cases it is impossible or undesirable to use bolts, especially if the parts have to be dismantled regularly as this causes wear on the thread which can result in thread breakage in cast iron. To overcome this studs are used, and these are fixed permanently in place by means of a stud box. When assembling, a nut is tightened on the stud just as if it were a bolt.

WASHERS, Fig. 181

It is usual to tighten up a nut on to a smooth steel collar known as a washer. This not only provides the nut with a full smooth bearing surface but helps the tightening up operation to be performed more easily by the slight rotation of the washer during the process.

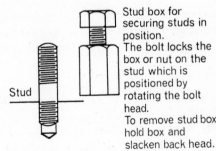

Stud box for securing studs in position.
The bolt locks the box or nut on the stud which is positioned by rotating the bolt head.
To remove stud box, hold box and slacken back head.

Stud

Fig. 180

160

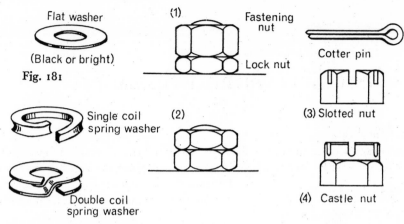

Flat washer

(Black or bright)

Fig. 181

(1) Fastening nut

Lock nut

Cotter pin

(3) Slotted nut

Single coil spring washer

(2)

Double coil spring washer

(4) Castle nut

Fig. 182   Locking Devices

LOCKING DEVICES, Fig. 182

LOCK NUTS

Owing to the danger of nuts working loose, arrangements have to be made to fix them in position after tightening. The simplest method is to use a spring washer, consisting of one or two coils of strip spring steel. A better and safer method is to use a lock nut. This is screwed down first in the normal way and tightened up. It is held in position with a spanner while the main nut is screwed down to within a few degrees of its limit, when the lower nut is tightened back to the top one, two spanners being used. The top, or outer nut, now carries the load on the bolt.

   It is usual to make the lock nut thin for economy, but owing to the weakness of a very thin spanner, two equal nuts, of about three-quarters their normal thickness are used.

THE CASTLE NUT

This is a nut with an extra thickness on its outer face across which are cut diametrically three slots. These enable cotter or split pins to be located after the nut has been tightened up, and one of its slots lined up with a hole through the bolt.

THE SLOTTED NUT

A plain nut having no extra thickness, but with three slots cut diametrically across the outer end.

   On small work, a fibre or nylon collar is fitted in the nut which securely holds once it has been tightened up. This is invaluable where simplicity and lightness are vital as in aircraft work.

F*

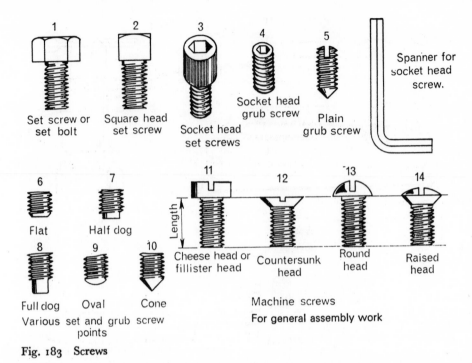

Fig. 183   Screws

SET SCREWS, Fig. 183

These are used to tighten one part to another and so prevent relative movement. They are threaded all their length, are normally of steel and case hardened for good-quality work.

GRUB SCREWS

Headless set screws used on revolving parts for safety.

SOCKET HEAD OR ALLEN SCREWS

These have a hexagonal hole in the head and are used for set-screw and grub-screw work.

Spanners, Fig. 184

Use.   For tightening or loosening nuts and bolts.

Material. Carbon steel or alloy steel.

Types.   Numerous, according to the special demands of the many trades and include single ended, double ended, box, ring and adjustable.

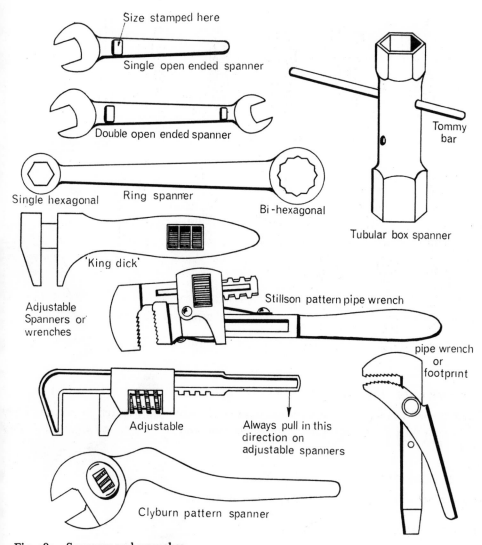

Size stamped here

Single open ended spanner

Double open ended spanner

Single hexagonal   Ring spanner

Bi -hexagonal

Tommy bar

Tubular box spanner

'King dick'

Adjustable
Spanners or
wrenches

Stillson pattern pipe wrench

pipe wrench
or
footprint

Adjustable

Always pull in this
direction on
adjustable spanners

Clyburn pattern spanner

Fig. 184 Spanners and wrenches

SINGLE OPEN-ENDED SPANNERS

The head is usually set over 15° for working in awkward corners.

DOUBLE OPEN-ENDED SPANNERS

Similar to the single ended but having a spanner at each end.

BOX SPANNERS

These are essential where the only approach to a nut is on the end. Rotation is by a steel rod, known as a tommy bar, which passes through holes in the tube.

RING SPANNERS

A good fitting tool which grips all faces of the nut. Cannot slip through the jaws spreading.

ADJUSTABLE SPANNERS OR WRENCHES

These tools are useful on odd sizes and for covering a variety of work, one jaw being adjustable by a screw arrangement.

KING DICK

Rather heavy but having good fitting jaws. Obtainable in four sizes from M10 to M30. Movement is by a knurled nut.

ADJUSTABLE SPANNER

A light useful tool. Movement is by a worm and rack.

CLYBURN PATTERN SPANNER

An adjustable spanner with a cranked arm. The sliding jaw has only a small travel but is a good fit.

THE STILLSON PATTERN PIPE WRENCH

Designed so that more effort on the handle increases the grip of the jaws on the pipe.

PIPE WRENCH OR FOOTPRINT

A simpler version of the Stillson wrench, the two parts being assembled by means of a knurled screw. Different holes enable a range of sizes to be covered.

SPANNER SIZES

The width of spanner jaws is found by the formula:

$$\text{Width across the jaws} = 1\tfrac{1}{2} \times \text{bolt diameter} + 3 \text{ mm.}$$

This is only approximate but very useful for the practical man.

18

Shaping and Milling Machines

Shaping machine

The shaping machine, Fig. 185, is used for the planing of small flat surfaces. On the front of the ram is mounted the tool head to which is fixed a clapper-box tool holder, the

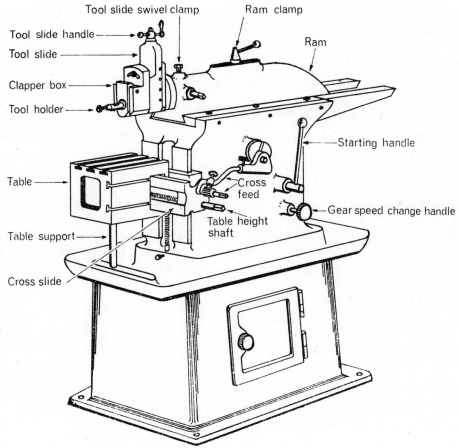

Fig. 185 Shaping machine

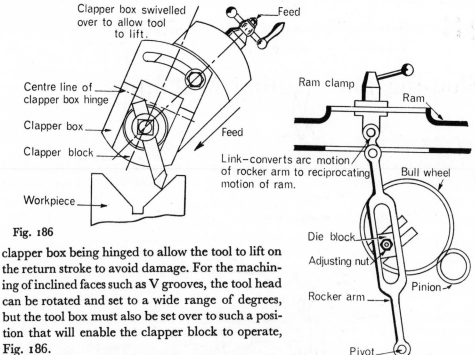

Clapper box swivelled over to allow tool to lift.

Feed

Centre line of clapper box hinge

Clapper box

Clapper block

Feed

Workpiece

Ram clamp

Ram

Link—converts arc motion of rocker arm to reciprocating motion of ram.

Bull wheel

Die block

Adjusting nut

Pinion

Rocker arm

Pivot

Fig. 186

Fig. 187

clapper box being hinged to allow the tool to lift on the return stroke to avoid damage. For the machining of inclined faces such as V grooves, the tool head can be rotated and set to a wide range of degrees, but the tool box must also be set over to such a position that will enable the clapper block to operate, Fig. 186.

The work can be clamped to the table but is more often held in a vice, which should be clamped to the table so that the jaws oppose the direction of the cut. By altering the position of the crank pin in the slotted link the length of the stroke can be altered and should be a little more than the actual cutting length to allow the tool to clear both ends of the workpiece, Fig. 187. The position of the stroke is then obtained by using the ram clamping nut or lever. The feed may be downwards by means of the tool feed-handle, or across by movement to the table depending upon the position of the workpiece. All adjustments must be made with the isolator switch off and no current used until the machine has been tried out by pulling the belt round by hand.

MOTION

In action, the tool will be seen to cut forward slowly then return quickly. This movement is called the Whitworth Quick Return Motion and is caused by the crank pin revolving at uniform angular velocity in a link hinged at one end. Consider the bull wheel rotating clockwise, then the time to travel from B to A, the forward cutting stroke must be longer than from A to B, the return stroke, Fig. 188. Typical shaping machine tools are shown in Fig. 189.

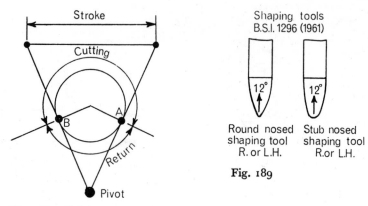

Stroke

Cutting

A

B

Return

Pivot

Fig. 188   Quick return motion

Shaping tools
B.S.I. 1296 (1961)

12°   12°

Round nosed   Stub nosed
shaping tool   shaping tool
R. or L.H.   R.or L.H.

Fig. 189

Motor

Overarm

Overarm support
bracket

Arbor

Table

Longitudinal feed

Cross slide handle

Knee bracket

Vertical movement
handle

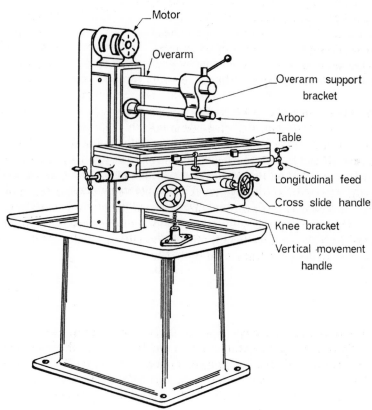

Fig. 190   Horizontal milling machine

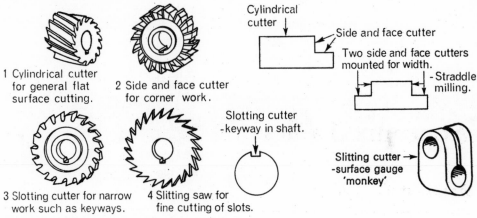

1 Cylindrical cutter for general flat surface cutting.

2 Side and face cutter for corner work.

Cylindrical cutter

Side and face cutter

Two side and face cutters mounted for width.

- Straddle milling.

Slotting cutter -keyway in shaft.

Slitting cutter → -surface gauge 'monkey'

3 Slotting cutter for narrow work such as keyways.

4 Slitting saw for fine cutting of slots.

Fig. 191   Milling cutters with **examples of work**

Horizontal milling machine

Of the several different kinds of milling machine, the horizontal type is probably the most popular, Fig. 190, and is used for machining surfaces flat or curved in a horizontal plane as well as cutting fine slits vertically. Cutters can also be assembled in a line for more complicated work, an operation known as 'gang' milling.

A knee bracket on the front of the machine supports the saddle on which is mounted a rectangular table for clamping the work. Alternatively a special vice can be used and must be clamped to the table with the jaws arranged to oppose the thrust from cutting. The drive is obtained from a hollow spindle mounted in the main casting. Unlike the lathe and shaper, the cutting tools are expensive, cannot be 'home-made' and must be sent back to the makers for re-sharpening. They are of many shapes and profiles ranging from cylinders with helical teeth to thin wheels like saw blades, Fig. 191. A central hole enables the tool to be mounted on the arbor where it is positioned by spacing collars. One end of the arbor fits into the driving spindle while the other end is supported by the overarm support bracket. Depth of cut is obtained by raising the table while the feed is supplied by moving the table horizontally either by hand or power, Fig. 192.

Extra care is required on this machine because more accidents have occurred operating it than any other, so keep your fingers away from the rotating cutter.

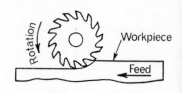

Rotation

Workpiece

Feed

Fig. 192   Milling

Appendix Tables

Iron and steel

METAL	CARBON CONTENT	REMARKS
Wrought iron	Trace	Resists corrosion and shock loads better than steel. Fibrous structure
Mild steel	Up to 0.3%	Has a wide use both for engineering and domestic articles, including nuts, bolts, washers, sheets, tubes and buckets. Sometimes known as case hardening steel being ideal for that purpose
Medium steel	0.3% to 0.6%	For more important work such as railway and automobile parts as well as structural use
High carbon steel	0.6% to 1.5%	Also known as Tool Steel, and Cast Crucible Steel. Can be hardened and tempered. Used for tool making, also for manufacture of strong steel castings
Silver steel	About 1.1%	A high carbon steel which has been ground to an exact size, and having a bright finish on its surface. In demand by tool makers
Cast iron	2.5% to 3.5%	Only part of the carbon is alloyed with this metal, the remainder existing in a free state as graphite. Although it is brittle it is valued because of the ease with which it can be cast into intricate shapes and its great strength in compression

Brass

NAME	COPPER %	ZINC %	TIN %	LEAD %	REMARKS
Gilding metal	85–95	15–5	—	—	A golden coloured brass much used in decorative metalwork and in cheap jewellery
Cartridge brass	70	30	—	—	A malleable brass ideal for cold working. May be deep drawn, stamped or spun. Used for the making of cartridge cases, hence its name
English standard brass	66	34	—	Trace	A general-purpose brass, ideal for machining because of lead content
Basis brass, also known as Common brass	62–64	38–36	—	—	A little harder and requires more frequent annealing than cartridge brass. Used in presswork for cheap products
Muntz metal, also know as Yellow metal and Drill rod	60	40	—	—	Owing to high zinc content is essentially a hot working alloy. Suitable for casting, pressing and hot stamping
Free cutting brass	58	$40\frac{1}{2}$	—	$1\frac{1}{2}$	A good brass for machine work. Can be cut at high speeds. Suitable for shaped work such as 'screw threads'. Tends to be 'hot short'

Screw threads

Tapping Drill Sizes for the Recommended Series for Screws, Bolts and Nuts.
NOTE.   The diameters given in Column 1 should be used in preference to those in Column 2.

Basic Major Diameters		Pitches		Tapping Drill Sizes			
		Coarse Series	Fine Series	Coarse Series		Fine Series	
1	2			Recommended	Alternative	Recommended	Alternative
2	—	0.4	—	1.6	1.65	—	—
—	2.2	0.45	—	1.75	1.8	—	—
2.5	—	0.45	—	2.05	2.1	—	—
3	—	0.5	0.35	2.5	2.55	2.65	2.7
—	3.5	0.6	0.35	2.9	2.95	3.15	3.2
4	—	0.7	0.5	3.3	3.4	3.5	—
—	4.5	0.75	0.5	3.7	3.8	4	—
5	—	0.8	0.5	4.2	4.3	4.5	—
6	—	1	0.75	5	5.1	5.2	5.3
—	7	1	0.75	6	6.1	6.2	6.3
8	—	1.25	1	6.8	6.9	7	7.1
10	—	1.5	1.25	8.5	8.6	8.8	8.9
12	—	1.75	1.25	10.2	10.4	10.8	10.9
—	14	2	1.5	12	12.2	12.5	12.6
16	—	2	1.5	14	—	14.5	14.6
—	18	2.5	1.5	15.5	—	16.5	—
20	—	2.5	1.5	17.5	—	18.5	—

This table has been compiled from B.S. 3643: Part I: 1963 and Supplement No. 1 (1967) to B.S. 1157: 1965.

Comparison Chart of Thread Sizes

ISO Metric	BA	BSW	BSF
2	9		
2.5	8		
	7		
	6		
3	5	$\frac{1}{8}$	
	4		
4	3		
5	2	3/16	3/16
	1		
6	0	$\frac{1}{4}$	$\frac{1}{4}$
8		5/16	5/16
10		$\frac{3}{8}$	$\frac{3}{8}$
12		7/16	7/16
		$\frac{1}{2}$	$\frac{1}{2}$

British Standard twist drill sizes, superseding drill gauge and letter sizes

Drill gauge and letter sizes of twist drills are now obsolete and should not be used in new designs. To assist users in securing the drill sizes required, the equivalent standard sizes are given below in bold type.

| Old drill gauge and letter size | | British Standard (international) series | | | Old drill gauge and letter size | | British Standard (international) series | | | Old drill gauge and letter size | | British Standard (international) series | | |
OLD SIZE	Decimal equivalent (in)	NEW SIZE (mm)	NEW SIZE (in)	Decimal equivalent (in)	OLD SIZE	Decimal equivalent (in)	NEW SIZE (mm)	NEW SIZE (in)	Decimal equivalent (in)	OLD SIZE	Decimal equivalent (in)	NEW SIZE (mm)	NEW SIZE (in)	Decimal equivalent (in)
80	0·0135	0·35		0·0138	45	0·0820	2·10		0·0827	10	0·1935	4·90		0·1929
79	0·0145	0·38		0·0150	44	0·0860	2·20		0·0866	9	0·1960	5·00		0·1968
78	0·0160	0·40		0·0157	43	0·0890	2·25		0·0886	8	0·1990	5·10		0·2008
77	0·0180	0·45		0·0177	42	0·0935		3/32	0·0938	7	0·2010	5·10		0·2008
76	0·0200	0·50		0·0197	41	0·0960	2·45		0·0965	6	0·2040	5·20		0·2047
75	0·0210	0·52		0·0205	40	0·0980	2·50		0·0984	5	0·2055	5·20		0·2047
74	0·0225	0·58		0·0228	39	0·0995	2·55		0·1004	4	0·2090	5·30		0·2087
73	0·0240	0·60		0·0236	38	0·1015	2·60		0·1024	3	0·2130	5·40		0·2126
72	0·0250	0·65		0·0256	37	0·1040	2·65		0·1043	2	0·2210	5·60		0·2205
71	0·0260	0·65		0·0256	36	0·1065	2·70		0·1063	1	0·2280	5·80		0·2283
70	0·0280	0·70		0·0276	35	0·1100	2·80		0·1102	A	0·2340		15/64	0·2344
69	0·0292	0·75		0·0295	34	0·1110	2·80		0·1102	B	0·2380	6·00		0·2362
68	0·0310		1/32	0·0312	33	0·1130	2·85		0·1122	C	0·2420	6·10		0·2402
67	0·0320	0·82		0·0323	32	0·1160	2·95		0·1161	D	0·2460	6·20		0·2441
66	0·0330	0·85		0·0335	31	0·1200	3·00		0·1181	E	0·2500		1/4	0·2500
65	0·0350	0·90		0·0354	30	0·1285	3·30		0·1299	F	0·2570	6·50		0·2559
64	0·0360	0·92		0·0362	29	0·1360	3·50		0·1378	G	0·2610	6·60		0·2598
63	0·0370	0·95		0·0374	28	0·1405		9/64	0·1406	H	0·2660		17/64	0·2656
62	0·0380	0·98		0·0386	27	0·1440	3·70		0·1457	I	0·2720	6·90		0·2717
61	0·0390	1·00		0·0394	26	0·1470	3·70		0·1457	J	0·2770	7·00		0·2756
60	0·0400	1·00		0·0394	25	0·1495	3·80		0·1496	K	0·2810		9/32	0·2812
59	0·0410	1·05		0·0413	24	0·1520	3·90		0·1535	L	0·2900	7·40		0·2913
58	0·0420	1·05		0·0413	23	0·1540	3·90		0·1535	M	0·2950	7·50		0·2953
57	0·0430	1·10		0·0433	22	0·1570	4·00		0·1575	N	0·3020	7·70		0·3031
56	0·0465		3/64	0·0469	21	0·1590	4·00		0·1575	O	0·3160	8·00		0·3150
55	0·0520	1·30		0·0512	20	0·1610	4·10		0·1614	P	0·3230	8·20		0·3228
54	0·0550	1·40		0·0551	19	0·1660	4·20		0·1654	Q	0·3320	8·40		0·3307
53	0·0595	1·50		0·0591	18	0·1695	4·30		0·1693	R	0·3390	8·60		0·3386
52	0·0635	1·60		0·0630	17	0·1730	4·40		0·1732	S	0·3480	8·80		0·3465
51	0·0670	1·70		0·0669	16	0·1770	4·50		0·1772	T	0·3580	9·10		0·3583
50	0·0700	1·80		0·0709	15	0·1800	4·60		0·1811	U	0·3680	9·30		0·3661
49	0·0730	1·85		0·0728	14	0·1820	4·60		0·1811	V	0·3770		3/8	0·3750
48	0·0760	1·95		0·0768	13	0·1850	4·70		0·1850	W	0·3860	9·80		0·3858
47	0·0785	2·00		0·0787	12	0·1890	4·80		0·1890	X	0·3970	10·10		0·3976
46	0·0810	2·05		0·0807	11	0·1910	4·90		0·1929	Y	0·4040	10·30		0·4055
										Z	0·4130	10·50		0·4134

B.S. Data Sheet 328A: 1963, 'Twist drill sizes, superseding drill gauge and letter sizes' is reproduced by permission of the British Standards Institution, 2 Park Street, London, W.1.

Recommended speeds for 6.4 mm diam. 'Presto' H.S.S. twist drill

Metal	R.P.M.
Aluminium	3,650
Brass, soft	2,300
Brass, hard	925
Cast Iron, soft	1,825
Mild Steel	1,500
Carbon Steel	750

Table of wire and sheet gauge sizes in millimeters

I.S.W.G. No.	Millimetres
10	3.25
11	2.95
12	2.64
13	2.34
14	2.03
15	1.83
16	1.63
17	1.42
18	1.22
19	1.02
20	0.91
21	0.81
22	0.71
23	0.61
24	0.56
25	0.51
26	0.46
27	0.42
28	0.38
29	0.35
30	0.32

Book List

CAMM, F. J. *Practical Mechanic's Handbook*, 8th edn. Newnes, 1960
DEARDEN, J. *Iron and Steel Today*, 2nd edn. O.U.P., 1956
DERRY, T. K. and WILLIAMS, T. I. *A Short History of Technology*. O.U.P., 1960
GLOAG, J. *The English Tradition in Design*. A. & C. Black, 1959
OMAN, CHARLES. *English Domestic Silver*, 4th edn. A. & C. Black, 1959
REDMAYNE, P. B. *The Changing Shape of Things*. Murray, 1945
SANDHAM, R. and WILLMORE, F. R. *Metalwork*. E. Arnold, 1962
SHIRLEY, A. J. and SHIRLEY, A. F. *Handicraft in Metal*, 6th edn. Batsford, 1953
SMITH, DONALD. *Metalwork: An Introductory Historical Survey*. Batsford, 1956
The Blacksmith's Craft. Rural Industries Bureau
Wrought Ironwork. Rural Industries Bureau

The British Iron and Steel Federation, Steel House, Tothill Street, London, S.W.1: Booklets and visual aids.

The Aluminium Development Association, 33 Grosvenor Street, London, W.1: Booklets and visual aids.

British Standards Institution, 2 Park Street, London, W.1: Sales Branch 101–113 Pentonville Road, London, N.1.

C.S.E. Examination Questions

The Publishers are grateful to the following C.S.E. Regional Boards for permission to include specimen questions from their papers: Associated Lancashire Schools Examining Board, East Anglian Regional Examinations Board, East Midland Regional Examinations Board, Middlesex Regional Examining Board, North Western Secondary Schools Examinations Board, South East Regional Examinations Board, Southern Regional Examinations Board, Welsh Joint Education Committee, West Midlands Examinations Board.

PART I—THEORY

SECTION A—Questions which require short answers and simple sketches where possible.

1. Name a metal from which each of the following is usually made :
   (*a*) a surface plate; (*b*) a centre punch;
   (*c*) a soldering bit; (*d*) a twist drill. (WEST MIDLANDS)

2. What is tinplate? Give one common use of tinplate. (WEST MIDLANDS)

3. Give TWO reasons for the flutes on a Morse twist drill. (WEST MIDLANDS)

4. Name the part of the lathe in which the drill chuck or dead centre is usually fitted. (ASSOC. LANCS)

5. The tip of a soldering bit is coated with solder before being used. What is this process called? (ASSOC. LANCS)

6. What is the name of the lathe slide which can be adjusted for taper turning? (ASSOC. LANCS)

7. What type of file has a safe edge? (ASSOC. LANCS)

8. How should you anneal (*a*) copper, and (*b*) aluminium? (SOUTHERN REG.)

9. What is meant by planishing and what is its main purpose? (SOUTHERN REG.)

10. Give the full names and an example of the use of the following abbreviations: H.S.S., M.S., R.P.M. (SOUTHERN REG.)

11. How may a circular split die be adjusted? Why is adjustment necessary? (SOUTHERN REG.)

12. Which material would you:
    (i) case harden; (ii) harden and temper? (SOUTHERN REG.)

13. Make labelled sketches to explain what is meant in tin-plate work, by:
    (i) a safe edge or beaded edge; (ii) a wired edge. (SOUTHERN REG.)

14. Which hand tool would you use to cut:
    (i) 12 mm diameter mild steel; (ii) 0.8 mm copper sheet? (SOUTHERN REG.)

15. Make a simple freehand sketch of a 'set screw' and a 'grub screw'.   (SOUTHERN REG.)

16. What precautions would you take to prevent damage to a hack-saw blade when sawing?
     (WELSH JOINT)

17. (a) When is a pilot hole used in drilling?
     (b) Why is it used?   (WELSH JOINT)

18. (a) Why must a flux be used when soft soldering?
     (b) What flux should be used for soldering electrical connections?
     (c) Why should that flux be used?   (WELSH JOINT)

19. (a) Why is there a 'set' on the teeth of a hacksaw blade?
     (b) Which way should the teeth point when the blade is in the frame?   (MIDDLESEX)

20. Make a simple sketch indicating the *rake* and *clearance* on a lathe tool.   (MIDDLESEX)

21. Why is a soldering 'iron' made with a copper bit?   (MIDDLESEX)

22. How would you clean a file which has become 'pinned' in use?   (MIDDLESEX)

23. State TWO ways of forming metals into shapes.   (MIDDLESEX)

24. Name TWO abrasives used for polishing metals.   (NORTH WESTERN)

25. What is meant by the term *a blind hole*?   (NORTH WESTERN)

26. Give THREE ways by which two pieces of metal may be joined together.
     (NORTH WESTERN)

27. Some household articles are made of metal.   Name ONE article made from EACH of the following:
     (a) Brass; (b) Iron; (c) Aluminium; (d) Steel; (e) Copper.   (NORTH WESTERN)

28. Name the process in which a round bar 10 mm in diameter is reduced to a point by forging.
     (NORTH WESTERN)

29. Give TWO uses for the tailstock of a lathe.   (NORTH WESTERN)

30. What kind of mallet would you use to hollow a copper bowl?   (SOUTH EAST REG.)

31. What acid is usually used in school workshops to remove the oxide film after annealing copper?
     (SOUTH EAST REG.)

32. What would you use to stop the top and bottom parts of a two-part sand mould from sticking together?   (SOUTH EAST REG.)

33. Name a tool you would use to check the inside diameter of a tube.   (SOUTH EAST REG.)

34. What type of chuck would you use to hold square metal in the lathe?   (SOUTH EAST REG.)

35. Brass is an alloy of two metals. What are they?   (SOUTH EAST REG.)

36. What is the name of the soft stone that is used to remove file marks, or scratches from non-ferrous metals?   (SOUTH EAST REG.)

37. Why should you centre punch your work before drilling?   (EAST ANGLIAN)

38. How is copper annealed? (EAST ANGLIAN)

39. Sketch EITHER a half-moon stake OR a planishing hammer. (EAST ANGLIAN)

40. Copper is a good conductor of heat. Where is this property made use of in the workshop? (EAST ANGLIAN)

41. What is meant by the 'draw' on a pattern? (EAST MIDLANDS)

42. What is a cope and drag used for? (EAST MIDLANDS)

43. What is the main difference between lathe tools used for turning brass and those used for turning mild steel? (EAST MIDLANDS)

44. What is meant by the term annealing? (EAST MIDLANDS)

SECTION B—Questions which require longer and more detailed answers with sketches where possible.

1. What do you understand by the following terms?
   (a) sweating; (b) planishing; (c) pickling; (d) annealing. (WEST MIDLANDS)

2. When filing certain metals 'pinning' of the file teeth occurs.
   (a) What does this mean?
   (b) How can it be prevented?
   (c) What would you do if this occurred?
   (d) Sketch and name FOUR file sections, and give ONE example of the use of each file. (WEST MIDLANDS)

3. Explain the following foundry terms:
   (a) contraction rule; (b) draft; (c) core.
   (d) What safety precautions would you take when pouring a mould? (WEST MIDLANDS)

4. A 150 mm length of 16 mm diam. mild steel is required to be turned between centres. How would you.
   (a) prepare the steel bar;
   (b) mount the bar in the lathe ready for turning?
   Illustrate your answers with sketches. (WEST MIDLANDS)

5. Design a suitable clamp to which is affixed four coat hooks. The clamp is to fasten round a 50 mm diameter bell-tent pole for use when camping. State the main sizes and the material to be used. (SOUTHERN REG.)

6. A latch or fastener is required for a wrought iron gate that is 1 m wide. It is to be very simple in action, to open from either side, to slam shut, and yet hold securely. Make some small sketches of possible types and an enlarged finished sketch of the latch that you prefer. (SOUTHERN REG.)

7. Explain with the aid of sketches how you would use a surface gauge, or scribing block to mark off the position of a hole which has to be drilled central and true across the diameter of a 25 mm diameter bar of mild steel. (SOUTHERN REG.)

8. If you were making the stock of a try square from 20 mm × 10 mm bright drawn mild steel, how would you check the two opposite faces for flatness and parallelism? (SOUTHERN REG.)

9. Draw dimensioned sketches of a bracket for a rear lamp of a bicycle. Assume that the socket in the lamp is 30 mm wide and the diameter of the rear fork of the bicycle is 12 mm.

(WELSH JOINT)

10. Describe with sketches, the hand tools used in cutting internal and external threads. When making a nut and bolt, which thread is cut first? Give the reason for this. (WELSH JOINT)

11. Describe in detail how you would harden and temper a centre punch. (WELSH JOINT)

12. (a) Draw the cross-section of a pair of moulding boxes assembled ready for pouring after the pattern has been drawn.
(b) How would you make a simple cylindrical core?
(c) Explain THREE faults which can spoil a casting. (MIDDLESEX)

13. Consider the jobs you have made during the past year and make a large dimensioned sketch of the one you liked best.
Make a list of the main steps in its construction illustrated with sketches where necessary.

(MIDDLESEX)

14. Describe, in note form with the aid of sketches, the processes and metal used to make a cold chisel. (NORTH WESTERN)

15. Describe, with the aid of sketches, the function of FIVE of the following tools:
(a) inside calipers;   (b) outside calipers;   (c) a centre square;
(d) a centre punch;   (e) odd leg calipers;   (f) a try-square;
(g) a surface gauge;   (NORTH WESTERN)

16. You are required to make a leak-proof tray for a plant stand. The tray is to be made from light gauge metal and is to be 400 mm long and 100 mm wide by 25 mm deep. Sketch the development, explain how you would make the tray and say what finish you would give to the edges. (NORTH WESTERN)

17. Explain how you would make the following in Tin Plate:
(a) a folded and grooved seam; (b) a wired edge.
Sketch one example of a job in which each might be used. (SOUTH EAST)

18. Name THREE methods involving the use of heat for joining metals. Give details of ONE of these three methods, naming the tools and materials used. (EAST ANGLIAN)

19. With the aid of sketches describe the processes of *hollowing* and *raising*. Give an outline drawing of a form suitable for hollowing and a form suitable for raising.

(NORTH WESTERN)

20. Explain with the aid of sketches how you would form a scroll with flared ends on one of a number of pieces 12 mm × 4 mm black mild steel.
Name three tools you would use to form the scrolls. (EAST MIDLANDS)

21. You are required to find the centre of the end of a 300 mm long piece of 50 mm diameter B.D.M.S. bar. Describe two methods by which you could centre the end of the bar.

(EAST MIDLANDS)

22. What is an oddside pattern?

    Explain with the aid of sketches how you would mould from this type of pattern, assuming the moulding sand is prepared for use. (EAST MIDLANDS)

23. Sketch the longitudinal section of a blacksmiths forge, show and name all the details on your sketch. (EAST MIDLANDS)

PART II—PRACTICAL

This part of the Examination may consist of a practical test or a project depending on the syllabus being followed.

The selected work will be attempted within a maximum workshop time of 8 hours.

1. A table lamp is required to give a shaded background light while viewing television, the lamp will be stood on top of the television set for this purpose.

   You are required to make a suitable lamp, the fitting to hold the bulb will require a hole tapped to allow the bulb fitting to be screwed into the top of the lamp.

   You should also show on your planning drawing the shape of a shade that would be suitable for the lamp you have designed.

   The shade is NOT to be made in the practical examination. (EAST MIDLANDS)

2. A condiment set (salt, pepper and mustard) is to be given for a wedding present.

   You are required to plan and make the salt OR pepper pot; the final finish should be suitable to allow the article to be silver plated, or stainless steel may be used. (EAST MIDLANDS)

3. A budgerigar breeder requires a small self-feeding hopper for his aviary, to allow seed to be available over a period of two or three days after each filling.

   Provision should be made for hanging the hopper to the wire or side of the aviary, and a perch provided approximately 48 mm from the front edge of the trough, this should consist of a piece of 6 mm or 8 mm diameter wood dowel.

   The size of the hopper should be approximately 125 mm long and 125 mm high. (A self feeding hopper allows the birds to feed from the bottom and further seed can drop down from the hopper to keep the feeding trough full.) (EAST MIDLANDS)

4. A small screwdriver is required for a cycle tool kit, the handle may be made of any suitable material and should be comfortable to hold. You should state clearly on your drawing the type of material or materials you use for this article.

   The maximum length of the screwdriver has to be 165 mm, and the blade width at the tip of the screwdriver should be 5 mm.

   ONE SIDE of the blade tip should be left unpolished after heat treatment. (EAST MIDLANDS)

5. A decorative grill is required to form a panel at the top of a staircase. The area to be filled by the panel is surrounded by the woodwork of the staircase, the woodwork being 75 mm in width.

   The overall size of the panel has to be 600 mm and 300 mm, suitable means should be allowed for the panel to be fastened to the woodwork by No. 6 countersunk wood screws.

   (EAST MIDLANDS)

Five hours of workshop time will be allowed to make the article you have planned. You may make any necessary modifications to your design.

6. Design a paper punch suitable for punching a single hole in up to 12 sheets of paper. The hole punched is to be 6 mm diameter with its centre 12 mm from the edge of the paper. There is no restriction on equipment or material. If you wish to include a casting in your design, the pattern may be made and the metal poured before the date of the practical examination.

(EAST ANGLIAN)

7. Design in non-ferrous metal a small combined stand and tray to hold a wristlet watch and small change. The article should be so designed that the watch can be read without being moved. It is anticipated that such a fitment would be kept on a bedside cabinet.

(EAST ANGLIAN)

Index